150 MORE CAPTIVATING CHEMISTRY EXPERIMENTS USING HOUSEHOLD SUBSTANCES

By BRIAN ROHRIG

Other Books by Brian Rohrig:

150 Captivating Chemistry Experiments Using Household Substances
101 Intriguing Labs, Projects, and Activities for the Chemistry Classroom
39 Amazing Experiments with the Mega-Magnet
39 Fantastic Experiments with the Fizz-Keeper
39 Dazzling Experiments with Dry Ice
39 Spectacular Experiments with Soda Pop

All books can be ordered directly from FizzBang Science

Published by FizzBang Science
807 Murlay Drive
Plain City, Ohio 43064
www.fizzbangscience.com
info@fizzbangscience.com

ISBN 0-9718480-1-7

12 11 10 9 8 7 6 5 4

For Bradley

Cover design by Kristi Gerner.

Text edited by Frank Reuter.

Printed by Network Printers in Milwaukee, Wisconsin.

ACKNOWLEDGMENTS:

Many of the experiments in this book are based upon the work of others. I have attempted to acknowledge all whose work I have built upon. I owe a debt of gratitude to everyone mentioned below. I sincerely apologize for any omissions.

I first learned of the following experiments from these individuals:

"Fun With Tonic Water," **Jeff Bracken**, chemistry teacher at Westerville North High School in Westerville, OH.

"Do Light Bulbs Really Burn?" **Lee Marek** of Weird Science and Naperville North High School in Naperville, IL.

"Magic Balls, The Mysterious Disappearing Fluid, and Preventing Green Egg Yolks," **Rhonda Reist**, chemistry teacher at Olathe North High School, Olathe, KS.

"The Incredible Expanding Ivory Soap, Vacuum Pack A Person, Shrinking A Styrofoam Cup, and Testing Margarine For Fat Content," **Bob Becker**, chemistry teacher at Kirkwood High School, Kirkwood, MO.

"The Evaporation Race," **Dave Katz**, chemistry professor, Cabrini College, Radnor, PA.

"Making A Flowmotion Tube," **Pat Funk**, chemistry teacher, Pataskala High School, Pataskala, OH.

"A Miniature Lava Lamp, The Amazing Windbag," **Steve Spangler**, Director Regis Institute of Chemical Education, Regis University, Denver, CO.

"Bowling For Density," **Mike Horton**, chemistry/physics teacher, Perris High School, Perris, CA.

"Acid/Base Tie-Dye," **Adam Bush**, former student.

"Toilet Paper Streamers," **Gene Easter**, chemistry/physics teacher, Streetsboro High School, Streetsboro, OH.

"Why Ripe Bananas Taste Sweet, Natural Acid/Base Indicators, Polymer Worms, Testing Fruit Drinks For Calcium, and Making Orange Sherbet," **Dr. Susan Hershberger**, chemistry professor, Miami University, Miami, OH.

I first saw "Why Soda Does Not React With An Aluminum Can" at SECO 2001 in Cincinnati, OH by a group of chemistry teachers in honor of **Dr. Cliff Schrader**, longtime chemistry teacher in Dover, OH.

The following experiments are based on the following sources:

"Does Ice Melt Faster In Fresh or Salt Water?" **Annis Hapkiewicz**, *Authentic Research Within the Grasp of High School Students,* JCE, Sept. 1999, pp. 1212-1215.

"Making An Electrorheological Fluid," **David Haase**, *Electrorheological Liquids*, The Physics Teacher, Vol. 31, April 1993.

"The Incredible Floating Yen," **Educational Innovations**, Norwalk, Conn.

"Reduction and Oxidation of Iodine, Parts 1 & 2," **Carl H. Snyder**, *The Extraordinary Chemistry of Everyday Things, 3rd edition, John Wiley and Sons, 1998.*

"Mrs. Stewart's Liquid Bluing Crystal Garden," from a pamphlet distributed by the manufacturers of **Mrs. Stewart's Liquid Bluing**.

"Shattering A Marble," **Joey Green**, *The Mad Scientist Handbook*, Berkely Publishing Group, New York, 2000.

"Fun With Jello," **Exploratorium web site:** http://www.exploratorium.edu/snacks/laser_jello/index.html

"A Novel Way To Clean Up An Oil Spill," **The NY Times Science Watch web site**, June 9, 1998, www.nytimes.com

"Matamucil Slime," **The page that dripped slime website.** www.freeweb.pdq.net

"Is Hot Air Less Dense Than Cold Air?" Physics lecture demonstrations with some problems and puzzles, too website. Compiled and annotated by **Donald Simanek**. www.lhup.edu/~dsimanek/scenario/demos.htm

In addition, the following reference sources were invaluable in compiling this book:

Fun with Chemistry: Vol. 2. Institute for Chemical Education. Compiled and edited by Mickey and Jerry Sarquis, Miami University, OH, 1993.

Chemical Activities. Christie Borgford and Lee R. Summerlin, ACS, 1988.

On Food and Cooking: The Science and Lore of the Kitchen. Harold McGee, Simon and Schuster, NY, 1984.

Polymer Chemistry, Revised Edition. Robert Lipscomb, NSTA, Arlington, VA, 1995.

TABLE OF CONTENTS

CHAPTER 1: DENSITY

CHAPTER 2: AIR PRESSURE

CHAPTER 3: GAS LAWS

CHAPTER 4: PHASE CHANGES

CHAPTER 5: PROPERTIES OF LIQUIDS

CHAPTER 6: PROPERTIES OF SOLIDS

CHAPTER 7: SOLUTIONS AND SOLUBILITY

CHAPTER 8: CHEMICAL REACTIONS

CHAPTER 9: ACIDS AND BASES

CHAPTER 10: POLYMERS

CHAPTER 11: ENERGY

CHAPTER 12: ELECTRICITY AND MAGNETISM

CHAPTER 13: LIGHT

CHAPTER 14: EDIBLE CHEMISTRY

INTRODUCTION

This book picks up where the first volume, *150 Captivating Chemistry Experiments Using Household Substances*, left off. In the four years since the first volume was published, thousands of teachers and parents have introduced their kids to the joys of household chemistry. The response to the first volume has been so gratifying that I felt the need to continue with another book of quality chemistry experiments that can be done at home. Just as in the first book, each experiment can be done with minimal expense. All of the experiments require only materials that can be found around the house. In those few instances where special materials are required, the expense is minimal and purchasing sources are identified. My goal is to make chemistry accessible to all students, whether in kindergarten or in high school.

This book is written at the high school level. However, most of the experiments can easily be adapted to a younger audience. I have performed most of these experiments with my high school chemistry students, and many with elementary students during summer chemistry camps.

Each experiment is designed to illustrate a profound concept in a clear and concise way. Each experiment can be used as a demonstration, student activity, or a take-home lab. However you use this book, you can be confident that each experiment has been thoroughly tested and will generate student enthusiasm.

When I walk into a grocery, drug, or hardware store, I see a vast chemical warehouse with unlimited potential. Hopefully, you will develop this same attitude after using this manual. It is my hope that this book will provide you with many hours of enjoyment exploring the wonders of the world around you. Please feel free to contact me if you have any questions about the experiments or concepts contained in this manual.

Brian Rohrig
Plain City, Ohio

SAFETY PRECAUTIONS

Please read thoroughly before proceeding with the experiments in this book.

1. All experiments are to be done only with competent adult supervision.

2. Never taste or drink the product of any reaction, unless specifically instructed to do so.

3. Never inhale any chemical substance. If you must smell something, wave your hand over the opening of the container and gently waft fumes towards your nose.

4. Always wear safety goggles when doing any experiment.

5. Always have a fire extinguisher nearby when using open flames.

6. Never add water to an acid. Always add acids to water.

7. If you spill a chemical on your skin, immediately wash it off with copious amounts of water.

8. If a chemical splashes in your eyes, rinse eyes thoroughly under water for 15 minutes and seek outside medical help immediately.

9. Always read the label of any chemical thoroughly before using.

10. Dispose of any chemical only according to the instructions on the label.

11. Store all chemicals out of the reach of children.

12. If smoke or fumes are produced, only perform the experiment under a fume hood or outside.

13. Never heat a closed container.

14. Keep all flammables away from open flame.

15. If you have long hair, tie it back when working around flames.

16. Do not wear loose-fitting or baggy clothing when working with flames or chemicals.

17. Wash hands thoroughly when finished.

CHAPTER 1
DENSITY

Density is defined as the amount of space a certain amount of matter occupies. Since 1 gram of water occupies a volume of 1 milliliter, water has a density of 1 g/mL.

Density can also be defined as a measure of how far apart the molecules are within a substance. Substances like gases have a very low density because their molecules are very far apart. Solids have a higher density because their molecules are closer together.

Mass refers to how much matter exists within an object. Matter is composed of atoms, which are the building blocks of all substances. The basic metric unit of mass is the gram.

Volume refers to how much space an object occupies. The bigger an object is, the greater its volume. The basic metric unit of volume is the Liter.

Buoyant force refers to the force that liquids or gases exert on other objects. The buoyant force always acts upward, and is responsible for keeping objects afloat in water, or making things rise in the air, like a helium balloon.

In this chapter, we will explore the fascinating world of density. Since density affects so many natural phenomena, it is an excellent place to begin our study of chemistry . . .

Density – Experiment # 1:
THE INCREDIBLE EXPANDING IVORY SOAP

Objective: To discover why a bar of Ivory Soap floats.

Materials:
- Bar of Ivory Soap
- Bars of various other brands of soap
- Microwave oven

Safety Precautions: The bar of Ivory soap will be hot when removed from microwave oven. Exercise caution.

Procedure:
1. Place bars of various brands of soap in a basin full of water. Most will sink.
2. Now place a bar of Ivory soap in the basin. It will float.
3. Place the bar of Ivory soap on a paper towel and place in the center of a microwave oven.
4. Turn the microwave oven on high for 2 - 3 minutes. The bar of Ivory soap will expand to fill nearly the entire oven!

Explanation: Ivory is one of the few bars of soap that floats. It floats because it has air pumped into it during its manufacture. When heated, the molecules of air begin to move faster, causing them to move farther apart. As a result of this, the Ivory soap expands to an incredible size. This is verification of Charles' Law, which states that as the temperature of a gas increases, its volume increases as well. Other bars of soap will tend to get hot and melt in the microwave. If you find another bar of soap that floats, see if it too will expand in the microwave oven.

The original introduction of air into Ivory soap was accidental. While a batch was being made by an employee for Proctor and Gamble, he forgot to turn off his mixing machine before taking a lunch break. This caused so much air to be whipped into the mixture that it floated. Public reaction was so positive to this floating soap that Proctor and Gamble began intentionally introducing air into the mixture. "It Floats" was added to Ivory's slogan in 1891.

Density – Experiment # 2:
A LIQUID RAINBOW

Objective: To create a liquid density column composed of all the colors of the visible light spectrum.

Materials:

- Sugar
- Food coloring
- Six empty milk jugs
- Glass test tube (or any tall, narrow drinking glass or bottle)
- Long-stemmed eyedropper or plastic pipette

Safety Precautions: None

Procedure:
1. To the first milk jug, add five cups of sugar, one container of red food coloring, and enough water to make one gallon.
2. To the second milk jug, add four cups of sugar, a mixture of red and yellow food coloring (see the food coloring package for exact proportions to use to make orange), and enough water to make a gallon of solution.
3. Repeat with the other four colors in separate milk jugs: for yellow, use three cups of sugar; for green use two cups of sugar; for blue use one cup of sugar; and for violet use no sugar.
4. Beginning with the red sugar solution, add about 5 mL to the test tube. (The amount added will vary, depending on the size of the test tube.)
5. Very carefully add 5 mL of orange solution on top of this. The best way is to very gently add it with an eyedropper so that it drips down the side of the tube.
6. Repeat with yellow, green, blue, and violet. The end result is a liquid density column composed of all the colors of the rainbow. Store upright and place a stopper or cork in the test tube to prevent it from evaporating.

Explanation: The solution with the greatest concentration of sugar will be the most dense. This will be the red sugar solution. Less dense solutions will float on top of more dense solutions. The violet solution, made with no sugar, is the least dense, which is why it will float on top. Solutions need to be added very slowly and carefully to one another, so as to prevent mixing.

Density – Experiment # 3:
THE MAGIC BALLS

Objective: To demonstrate that a more dense substance will sink in a less dense substance, and that a more dense substance will support the weight of a less dense substance.

Materials:

- Large transparent plastic container with lid
- Popcorn kernels
- Ping-pong ball
- Steel ball that is roughly the same size as the ping-pong ball

Safety Precautions: None

Procedure:

1. Fill the large plastic container about halfway with popcorn kernels.
2. Place the ping-pong ball on the bottom of the container, and gently rest the steel ball on top of the kernels.
3. Replace the lid and shake vigorously.
4. The steel ball will appear to have "magically" changed into the ping-pong ball.

Explanation: The steel ball is denser than the popcorn kernels, so when they are shaken up, the steel ball will fall to the bottom. The ping-pong ball is less dense than the kernels, so it will be forced upward by the kernels. The steel ball appears to have magically changed into a ping-pong ball, but in reality the balls have simply changed places.

Since kernels in motion exhibit fluid-like behavior, this experiment provides an excellent analogy for buoyant forces. More dense fluids exert a greater buoyant force than less dense fluids. Since the popcorn kernels act like the molecules of a fluid, they exert a buoyant force great enough to keep the ping-pong ball afloat, but not the steel ball. In order to cause the ping-pong ball to rise to the top, the kernels must be moving, which is always true of the molecules of a fluid.

Density – Experiment # 4:
IS HOT AIR LESS DENSE THAN COLD AIR?

Objective: To demonstrate that hot air is pushed upward by cold air due to density differences.

Materials:

- Electric drill
- Board approximately 48 inches long, 12 inches wide, and one-half inch thick.
- Large wooden matches

Safety Precautions: Perform only under adult supervision. Exercise caution with matches. Keep a fire extinguisher nearby.

Procedure:

1. Using the drill, drill a series of holes in the board in a vertical line approximately 1 inch apart and in each case completely through the board, extending the entire length of the board. The diameter of each hole needs to be of sufficient diameter to allow the matches to fit snugly. Leave a space of about 3 inches on both the top and on the bottom of the board where no holes are drilled.
2. Place a match in each hole, making sure they are each inserted to the same depth.
3. Place the board upright, holding the top of the board and allowing the board to rest on its bottom edge. Light the top match. Observe.
4. Now light the bottom match. Observe.

Explanation: When the top match is lit, only this match burns. But when the bottom match is lit, each match is lit in turn until they are all consumed. This experiment graphically shows that as the air around a match is heated, the buoyant force of the cold air underneath pushes it up. The buoyant force of the surrounding air pushes the flame of each match upward. This explains why campfires should always be lit from the bottom.

It is important that there be no side drafts, or this experiment will not work. If there is a side draft, attempt to eliminate it or stand in front of it to block it. It is interesting to note that the flames will nearly go out when they are about halfway up the board. This is because as the air underneath is heated, it becomes less dense and exerts less of a buoyant force on the air above. As the flames begin to die down, the air beneath the matches cools again, and then begins to exert a greater buoyant force on the air above. This clearly demonstrates that hot air does not rise by itself, but is pushed upward by cold air.

Density – Experiment # 5:
A MINIATURE SUBMARINE

Objective: To demonstrate how a real-life submarine is able to submerge and then rise in water.

Materials:

- Film canister
- Electric drill
- Tall graduated cylinder or 2-L bottle with top removed
- Alka-Seltzer tablets
- Pennies
- Citric acid (optional)
- Baking soda (optional)
- Baking powder (optional)

Safety Precautions: Wear safety goggles during this experiment.

Procedure:

1. Drill a small hole about 4 mm in diameter in the lid of the film canister using the electric drill.
2. Add just enough pennies to the canister so that it will sink. Remove one of the pennies, so the canister will now float.
3. Fill the canister with water, drop in a small piece of the Alka-Seltzer tablet and then replace the lid.
4. Quickly drop the canister – lid side down – into the graduated cylinder that is full of water. The canister should fall to the bottom, and after a short time rise back up to the top.
5. Optional – try these other combinations: baking powder and water, and baking soda and citric acid in place of the Alka-Seltzer.

Explanation: This experiment can be used as an open-ended investigation, where students are given only the materials and minimal instructions. They are then to discover for themselves how to construct the sub.

The first step is to add just enough pennies to make the canister sink, then remove one so that it floats. This is to ensure that when the Alka-Seltzer and water are added, the sub will be able to float back upward to the top. The amount of pennies will differ, because pennies minted before 1982 have a greater mass than those minted after 1982.

When the water and Alka-Seltzer are added, CO_2 gas will be produced, which will force water out of the small hole. It is essential that the hole be pointed downward, so that the water can be pushed out by the gas. If the hole is pointed upward, the gas will simply bubble up through the water without displacing it.

When the water is pushed out of the canister, the canister's mass is decreased. Since the volume of the sub remains constant, the density of the sub is therefore decreased. Now that the density has decreased, the buoyant force of the water is able to push the sub upward, causing it to rise. This is how real submarines operate. To sink, they take water into their ballast tanks, causing the sub to be denser than water. To rise, they expel water from their ballast tanks, making the sub less dense than water.

Other combinations that work are baking soda and citric acid, and baking powder and water. Both of these combinations produce carbon dioxide gas, which will displace water and cause the sub to rise.

Density – Experiment # 6:

KETCHUP PACKET CARTESIAN DIVER

Objective: To discover how changing the volume of a substance affects it density.

Materials:
- 2-Liter bottle
- Fizz-Keeper (available from grocery or department store)
- Variety of condiment packages, such as ketchup or mustard

Safety Precautions: Wear safety goggles. To avoid overpressurizing the bottle, do not pump up the bottle with the Fizz-Keeper more than 100 times. When releasing the pressure, unscrew the Fizz-Keeper slowly from the bottle. Never aim the Fizz-Keeper at another person, and never place your face directly over the Fizz-Keeper, especially when unscrewing it from the bottle. Never use the Fizz-Keeper on a glass bottle.

Procedure:
1. Fill the 2-Liter bottle most of the way with water.
2. Drop in a dozen or so condiment packages.
3. Attach the Fizz-Keeper. Make sure the water level is below the bottom of the Fizz-Keeper.
4. Pump up the Fizz-Keeper until the condiment packages have sunk to the bottom. Do not pump more than 100 times.
5. Remove the Fizz-Keeper slowly. Observe the condiment packages.

Explanation: The condiment packages contain air, which becomes compressed when the bottle is pumped up with air using the Fizz-Keeper. As the air in these packets is compressed, their volume decreases. This causes their density to increase, since their mass remains constant. The packets therefore sink to the bottom. When the pressure is lowered by removing the Fizz-Keeper, the packets rise because the air within them expands. This causes the density of the packets to decrease, since their volume has increased.

This experiment provides verification of Archimedes' Principle, which states that the buoyant force acting on an object is equal to the weight of the fluid displaced. Since the volume of the packets is decreased, they displace less water. Therefore the buoyant force exerted by the water is less – not enough to keep them afloat. This is also a good demonstration of Boyle's Law. Boyle's Law states that as the pressure on a gas is increased, its volume is decreased. It also states that as the pressure on a gas is decreased, its volume increases.

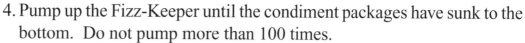

Density – Experiment # 7:
THE FLOATING GOLF BALL

Objective: To demonstrate that salt water is denser than fresh water.

Materials:
- Golf ball
- Salt (Rock salt or Kosher salt works best, since they are clear when dissolved in water.)
- Graduated cylinder or 2-L bottle with top removed

Safety Precautions: None

Procedure:
1. Add a golf ball to a cylinder of water. It will sink.
2. Pour a copious amount of salt into the cylinder and stir.
3. Drop in the golf ball. It will be magically suspended in the middle of the cylinder!

Explanation: Golf balls normally sink in water, as any golfer can attest. This is because golf balls are denser than water. By adding salt to the water, the density of the water is increased. Salt water can exert a greater buoyant force than fresh water, enabling objects such as golf balls to float. When the salt is added to the cylinder of water, much of it dissolves. When the golf ball is added, it will stay suspended somewhere around the middle of the cylinder, depending on how much salt was used. At this point the density of the salt water is equal to that of the golf ball. A density gradient is established in the cylinder, with the denser water being closer to the bottom. The golf ball will be floating on this layer of denser, saltier water yet at the same time will be on the bottom of a layer of less dense, less salty water. Since it is not possible to make out the distinction between the two layers, it appears as if the golf ball is in the center of a uniform layer. In actuality, the water becomes less salty toward the top of the cylinder, because more salt is concentrated on the bottom. As more salt on the bottom continues to dissolve, the density of the water will increase, causing the golf ball to gradually rise over time. This is fascinating to observe if the cylinder is covered and left undisturbed for several weeks.

Density – Experiment # 8:
THE GREAT GRAPE RACE

Objective: To demonstrate that denser fluids exert a greater buoyant force than less dense fluids.

Materials:
- Mountain Dew and Diet Mountain Dew (Mountain Dew works well due to its high sugar content)
- Grapes
- Transparent cups or large graduated cylinders

Procedure:
1. Fill one graduated cylinder with Mountain Dew, and the other with Diet Mountain Dew.
2. Drop a few green grapes into each, at exactly the same time.
3. The grapes will rise to the top more quickly in one container than in the other.

Explanation: The grapes in the regular Mountain Dew will rise more quickly than those in the Diet Mountain Dew. Since regular soda is denser due to its high sugar content, it exerts a greater buoyant force. The grapes are actually denser than both the regular and diet sodas, but they rise due to the attachment of many bubbles on their surface, causing them to become more buoyant. The bubbles act to increase the volume of the grapes without appreciably increasing their mass, thus making them less dense. Since regular soda is denser, not as many bubbles need to collect on the grapes before the buoyant force of the fluid pushes them upward. Since diet drinks are less dense, it takes more time for enough bubbles to collect before the buoyant force of the fluid can push the grapes up.

Density – Experiment # 9:

A MINIATURE LAVA LAMP

Objective: To construct a density column that resembles a miniature lava lamp.

Materials:
- 2-L preform (Order from FizzBang Science; alternately, a baby food jar may be used.)
- Tub Tints (available from toy store or order from FizzBang Science)
- Mineral oil

Safety Precautions: Mineral oil is poisonous. Keep out of reach of children.

Procedure:
1. Fill the preform about halfway with mineral oil. Add a Tub Tint.
2. Fill the preform the rest of the way with water. Add a few more tub tints of different colors. Replace the cap. Hold in an upright position for several minutes. Observe.

Explanation: Tub Tints are effervescent tablets that give off CO_2 gas upon contact with water. They were originally manufactured to color bath water and produce a fizzing sensation at the same time. When the Tub Tints are placed in mineral oil, they do not react. This is because mineral oil is a nonpolar substance, which usually will not dissolve substances that dissolve in water. When the Tub Tints are placed in water, the bubbles produced will be pushed to the top by the buoyant force of the fluid. As the bubbles pass through the mineral oil, they produce a lava-lamp effect. These bubbles will last for several minutes, and are truly spectacular to witness. Afterwards, you will have a permanent density column, which produces its own lava-lamp effect when turned upside down. The mineral oil, since it is less dense, will always be pushed upward by the more dense water.

Density – Experiment # 10:
IS IT REALLY GOLD?

Objective: To prove that a piece of fool's gold is not really gold by calculating its density.

Materials:
- Piece of pyrite (fool's gold)
- Sensitive balance
- Graduated cylinder or measuring cup
- Plastic cup
- Aluminum pie pan

Safety Precautions: None

Procedure:
1. Measure the mass of the piece of fool's gold, in grams, on a balance.
2. Fill the plastic cup to the brim with water and place in the pie pan.
3. Carefully drop in the piece of fool's gold.
4. Pour the water that overflowed in the pie pan into the graduated cylinder. Record the volume in mL.
5. Calculate the density in g/mL by dividing the mass by the volume.

Explanation: Throughout history, many people have been fooled into thinking they had discovered gold when they had actually found pyrite, which closely resembles real gold. But if they had known a little about density, they would not have made this mistake. Gold, being one of the densest elements, has a density of 19.3 g/mL. This means that 1 mL of gold has a mass of 19.3 grams. The densest element is osmium, which has a density of 22.4 g/mL. Pyrite, which is a compound composed of iron and sulfur, has a density of only 5.0 to 5.2 g/mL.

The formula for density is mass/volume. The mass of a sample of pyrite can be determined using a balance. Its volume can be determined by water displacement. When placed in a full cup of water, the amount of water that overflows represents what the sample displaced, which is equal to its volume. Your sample of pyrite will displace much more water than an equivalent mass of gold. If you happen to have a piece of gold, you can determine its volume in the same way!

Density – Experiment # 11:
BOWLING FOR DENSITY

Objective: To discover the difference in density between an 8 pound bowling ball and a 16 pound bowling ball.

Materials:
- 10 gallon aquarium
- 16 pound bowling ball
- 8 pound bowling ball

Safety Precautions: Do not drop bowling balls on your toes!

Procedure:
1. Carefully place the 16 pound bowling ball in the aquarium. Observe whether it sinks or floats.
2. Remove the 16 pound ball and place the 8 pound ball in the aquarium. Observe whether it sinks or floats.

Explanation: The 16 pound bowling ball will sink, while the 8 pound ball will float! Bowling balls were originally made of wood. In the early 1900's, hard rubber was used because it was more durable. In the 1970's, polyester balls were popular. In the early 1980's, a urethane shell was introduced, which is primarily used today. The core is generally denser, and is composed of polyester that may be infused with either calcium carbonate or barium sulfate. The type and amount of materials used are varied to make balls of the same size with different weights.

The radius of a typical bowling ball is from 10.8 to 10.9 cm. Assuming an average radius of 10.85 cm., a typical bowling ball will have a volume of 5350 cubic centimeters. This is calculated by using the formula for the volume of a sphere, which is $(4/3)\pi r^3$. This would make the density of an 8 lb. (3632 g) bowling ball .68 g/cc. This is calculated by using the formula for density, which is mass/volume. The density of a 12 lb. (5448 g) bowling ball would be 1.02 g/cc, and the density of a 16 lb. (7264 g) bowling ball would be 1.36 g/cc. Since water has a density of 1 g/cc, objects less dense than this will float, while those more dense will sink.

Density – Experiment # 12:
NEUTRAL BUOYANCY

Objective: To achieve neutral buoyancy.

Materials:
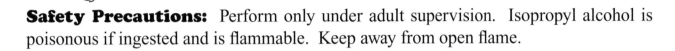
- Transparent plastic cup or beaker
- Olive oil
- 70% Isopropyl rubbing alcohol
- Eyedropper

Safety Precautions: Perform only under adult supervision. Isopropyl alcohol is poisonous if ingested and is flammable. Keep away from open flame.

Procedure: 1. Fill the cup about halfway with alcohol.
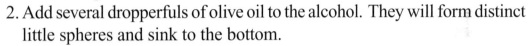
2. Add several dropperfuls of olive oil to the alcohol. They will form distinct little spheres and sink to the bottom.
3. Add water drop by drop until the balls of olive oil rise and become suspended in the middle of the water-alcohol solution.

Explanation: The olive oil initially sinks because it is denser than the alcohol. However, it is less dense than water. By adding water to the alcohol, the density of the alcohol-water solution is gradually increased, until it becomes equal to that of the olive oil. At this point, the olive oil will neither sink nor float, but will become suspended in a state of neutral buoyancy. The density of the olive oil is now equal to that of the surrounding solution. Fish, submarines, and the Goodyear Blimp can all experience neutral buoyancy if their density is equal to that of their surroundings.

The olive oil is interesting to observe because it forms many tiny little spheres when it is added to the water. The oil does not mix with water due to oil's nonpolar nature. Water molecules are polar, meaning they contain both a positive and a negative end. A nonpolar substance, such as oil, is completely neutral, so it does not readily mix with a polar substance. This property of the oil makes it easy to observe when neutral buoyancy has been achieved.

Density – Experiment # 13:
DOES CLAY FLOAT?

Objective: To make a boat from clay.

Materials: • Several pieces of modeling clay
               • Large basin of water

Safety Precautions: None

Procedure: 1. Drop the pieces of clay into the water to see if they float or sink.
               2. Attempt to fashion the pieces of clay into a boat that floats. Be creative.

Explanation: This experiment, though simple, illustrates many profound concepts. Nearly everyone will enjoy the challenge of trying to make a substance that is denser than water float. The key is to add air, which makes the volume of the clay boat much less than the volume of the original piece of clay. This is accomplished by making the clay very thin, with relatively tall sides to prevent water from entering. The addition of air to the boat adds a negligible amount of mass, but greatly increases its volume. Therefore the clay boat has a much lower density than the original piece of clay.

If the density of the original piece of clay is calculated by dividing its mass by its volume (density = mass/volume), it will have a density greater than that of water (1 g/cc). If the density of the clay boat is calculated, it will have a density less than that of water. Any substance that has a density less than that of water will float in water.

By forming the clay into a boat, it displaces more water. Archimedes' Principle states that the buoyant force that water exerts on an object is equal to the weight of water that object displaces. If the clay is made to displace more water, the water can exert a greater buoyant force on the clay, keeping it afloat. This is why boats can be made of steel or concrete – materials that are much denser than water. The key is to construct the boats in such a way that they trap enough air to give a volume increase sufficient to lower their density below that of water.

Density – Experiment # 14:
IS HOT WATER LESS DENSE THAN COLD WATER?

Objective: To discover the difference in density between hot and cold water.

Materials:
- Two balloons
- Hot water
- Basin of hot water

Safety Precautions: None

Procedure:
1. Fill one balloon with hot water from the tap.
2. Fill a second balloon with cold water.
3. Place both in a basin of hot water from the tap. What happens?

Explanation: The balloon filled with hot water will float and the balloon filled with cold water will sink! This happens because cold water is denser than hot water. As water is heated, its molecules move faster. This causes the molecules to spread apart from one another, causing the density of the water to decrease. As water cools, its molecules move slower. This causes the molecules to move closer together, causing the density of the water to increase.

Density – Experiment # 15:
THE RISING POP CAN

Objective: To discover whether air has a lower density than water.

Materials:
- Basin of water
- Pop can
- Rubber or plastic tubing

Safety Precautions: None

Procedure:

1. Fill a pop can with water and drop it into the basin of water.
2. Place one end of the hose into the can so it touches the bottom of the can.
3. Blow into the other end of the hose with your mouth. What happens?

Explanation: When you blow into the can, air displaces the water. Since air is less dense than water, the can will quickly rise to the top. This simple experiment has many practical applications. Submarines rise by forcing water out of their ballast tanks with air pressure. This lowers the submarine's density, which enables the buoyant force of the surrounding water to push it up.

When the water in the can is replaced by air, the volume of the can remains the same, yet its mass decreases. Therefore, its density decreases. Conversely, to make an empty can sink, it is necessary to increase its mass by adding water. Since the can's volume stays the same, its density increases.

Another way to make an empty can sink is to decrease its volume by flattening it. In this case, its density is increased because its mass remains constant. If you wanted to make this flattened can float again, it would be necessary to increase its volume, which would decrease its density.

Density – Experiment # 16:
OVERFLOWING ICE CUBES

Objective: To determine whether a glass full of water with ice cubes over the brim will overflow when the ice melts.

Materials:
- Glass of water
- Ice cubes

Safety Precautions: None

Procedure:
1. Fill a glass with water and then add ice cubes so that they are sticking out above the brim of the glass. Make sure all ice cubes are floating in the water.
2. Observe what happens to the water level when the ice cubes melt. Does the water level overflow?

Explanation: This is a classic experiment with intriguing results. Observation reveals that the water will not overflow, even though the ice was initially above the top of the glass. If you freeze a full glass of water, the ice will rise above the top of the brim because water expands as it freezes. If this ice melted, it would not overflow the glass, but would return to its original level. The expansion of water as it freezes makes it less dense than liquid water. Since the same mass occupies more volume, it becomes less dense.

If you examine the floating ice cubes, you will see that they are approximately 92% immersed underwater. This tells us that the density of ice is .92 g/cc. If an object is 10% immersed underwater, its volume would be .10 g/cc. It is easy to estimate the density of objects by measuring what percentage of the object is immersed underwater.

According to Pascal's Principle of Flotation, floating objects displace a mass of water equal to their own weight. If a ten ton ship is floating, it will displace ten tons of water. Archimedes' Principle states that the buoyant force that a fluid exerts on an object is equal to the weight of the water that object displaces. So the buoyant force acting on a ten ton floating ship is ten tons, which is exactly equal not only to the weight of water displaced but also to the weight of the ship itself.

If we assume each ice cube has a mass of 20 grams, this means each ice cube is displacing 20 grams of water. If 92% of the ice cube is underwater, this means 18.4 g of the ice cube is underwater and 1.6 g of the ice cube is above water. Yet the ice cube is displacing 20 g of water in the glass, since it has a mass of 20 g.

So when the ice cube melts, it does not overflow since it was already displacing 20 g of water when it was an ice cube. And, of course, a 20 g ice cube will melt into 20 g of water. So the water level cannot possibly overflow, because a 20 g floating ice cube and 20 g of liquid water take up the same amount of space in the glass of water.

Density – Experiment # 17:
THE MYSTERIOUS GRAPES

Objective: To discover how density affects whether objects sink or float.

Materials: • Green grapes
   • Two unopened bottles of Sprite

Safety Precautions: Do not drink Sprite after grapes have been added. Over time, mold and harmful bacteria will be produced.

Procedure: 1. Pour a little Sprite from each bottle to prevent overflow. Drop a handful of grapes into each bottle. Observe.
2. After several minutes, cap one bottle and leave the other uncapped. What happens to the grapes?
3. After a few minutes, uncap the capped bottle. What happens to the grapes?
4. Put the cap back on one bottle, and leave the other uncapped. Allow both to remain undisturbed.
5. After a day or so, check both bottles. What do you observe?

Explanation: The grapes will initially sink but then float as carbon dioxide bubbles are attracted to the outside of the grapes. This lowers their density, causing the grapes to be pushed up by the buoyant force of the surrounding fluid. The bubbles greatly increase the volume of the grapes, but only contribute negligibly to their mass. The bubbles act like tiny life preservers, which serve to make the grapes more buoyant.

When the cap is replaced, the grapes will eventually sink. They sink because CO_2 gas from the bottle enters the head space, causing an increase in pressure. This reduces the size of the bubbles. As a result, the volume of the grapes are not increased enough to cause them to rise. Removal of the cap will reduce the pressure, causing the bubbles to expand and the grapes to rise again. This is a good example of Boyle's Law, which states that increasing the pressure on a gas reduces its volume, and decreasing the pressure on a gas increases its volume.

In one or two days the grapes will float to the top in the bottle that was left uncapped, and will remain on the bottom in the capped bottle. This is because the grapes begin to undergo fermentation. The sugars in the grapes and the soda will react with yeast that is naturally found on the surface of the grapes to produce alcohol and CO_2 gas. When these grapes fill up with CO_2 gas, they float. In the capped bottle, the pressure of the carbon dioxide gas in the bottle will reduce the volume of the gas in these grapes; therefore they remain submerged. Since fermentation is an anaerobic process (occurring in the absence of oxygen), it can occur underwater.

Density – Experiment # 18:

DOES ICE MELT FASTER IN FRESH OR SALT WATER?

Objective: To determine the effect of the density of the surrounding fluid on the melting of ice.

Materials: • Colored ice cubes
  • Salt
  • Two large beakers or transparent bowls

Safety Precautions: None

Procedure: 1. Make two colored ice cubes by filling two plastic cups with colored water and freezing.
  2. Add one to a large beaker of tap water, and the other to a large beaker of salt water.
  3. Observe the rate of melting of each ice cube.

Explanation: The results of this experiment are quite a surprise when witnessed for the first time. The ice cube in the salt water melts much slower than the one in the fresh water. In the salt water the colored water from the melted ice cube forms a distinct layer that floats on top of the salt water. In the fresh water, the melted water sinks to the bottom and is evenly distributed.

These observations can be interpreted by comparing the density of fresh and salt water. When the ice melts, the water that results is very cold. It is more dense than the warmer water in the beaker, and will thus sink. As the colder water sinks, it displaces and pushes up the warmer water from the bottom. As this warmer water comes into contact with the ice cube, it hastens its rate of melting. A convection current has been set up, where the colder water sinks and the warmer water is pushed up. Convection is the transfer of heat by the movement of fluids.

In the beaker of salt water, the cold water that results from the melting of the ice cube is less dense than the salt water, so it floats on top. There are no convection currents occurring here. Since the ice cube is constantly in contact with very cold water, which prevents it from contacting the warmer water below, it takes a longer time to melt.

This phenomenon has many practical applications. Icebergs in the ocean last much longer than they do in fresh water. The melted ice from an iceberg will float on top of the salt water in the ocean, but will sink in fresh water. Ice cubes will cool a diet drink much faster than they will a sugared drink for this same reason.

I had an interesting experience with this phenomenon one summer at a camp I was conducting. Each morning I would make a five gallon container of Kool-Aid, and then place within it several large chunks of ice. When I emptied it in the afternoon, the ice cubes were usually still intact. This always intrigued me, because the Kool-Aid did not seem as cold as I would have liked. Then one morning while making the Kool-Aid I realized we were out of sugar. So I went ahead and made it without the sugar, adding the ice as usual. Later that morning, when I went to add the sugar, I noticed that the ice had completely melted! It is then I realized that adding ice to the sugary Kool-Aid only served to cool the top layer. Since we were getting the Kool-Aid from the bottom, the ice would have little cooling effect until the container was nearly empty. Agitation of the cooler before dispensing would probably be the best way to uniformly cool the drink.

CHAPTER 2
AIR PRESSURE

On the earth's surface, you are at the bottom of an ocean of air. This ocean of air is deepest at sea level, and gradually thins out into outer space several hundred miles up. The higher your altitude the less air pressure you experience, because the weight of the air above you is less.

At sea level, air pressure is exerting a pressure of 14.7 pounds per square inch (psi). This is sometimes referred to as simply 1 atmosphere (atm).

In this chapter, we will explore the awesome power of this invisible air pressure that constantly envelops us . . .

CRUSHING A CAN WITH AIR PRESSURE

Objective: To demonstrate the extraordinary power of the air by crushing a large metal can.

Materials:
- One gallon metal can (used for solvents such as acetone or alcohol)
- Hot plate or stove
- Ice

Safety Precautions: Make sure can is thoroughly free of any residual solvent before using – rinse can thoroughly and allow to dry completely before performing this experiment. Exercise caution not to burn yourself when boiling water or using a hot plate. Adult supervision is required.

Procedure:
1. Place a small amount of water in the can and heat to boiling over the hot plate, with the lid removed.
2. Heat the water until it is rapidly boiling, as evidenced by the steam condensing as it comes out of the hole.
3. Remove from heat and quickly place the cap on the can.
4. Pour ice water over the can. Observe.

Explanation: This is a classic experiment that vividly demonstrates just how powerful air pressure really is. When the water is heated within the can, it turns into steam. This steam forces out any air that is in the can. When removed from the heat and cooled, this steam condenses back into liquid water. Liquid water takes up much less space than steam, so when the steam condenses a near vacuum is created in the can. Outside air pressure, at 14.7 pounds per square inch (psi), easily crushes the can since there is little air in the can to push outward.

Air Pressure – Experiment # 2:
VACUUM PACK A PERSON

Objective: To demonstrate the concept of vacuum packing.

Materials:

- Large plastic garbage bag
- Piece of flexible window screen
- Rubber band
- Vacuum cleaner with hose
- Willing volunteer

Safety Precautions: Do this experiment only under adult supervision. Do not place bag around neck, or place head in bag. If the volunteer experiences any discomfort, shut off vacuum cleaner immediately.

Procedure:
1. Wrap the piece of screen around the opening of the vacuum cleaner hose with a rubber band, to prevent the bag from getting drawn up into the vacuum cleaner.
2. Under adult supervision, have a volunteer remove their shoes and kneel inside the bag, holding the hose tightly against the chest, with the opening of the hose pointed down.
3. Wrap the bag tightly around the shoulders, not around the neck, making sure that no air can enter.
4. Turn on the vacuum cleaner and observe. Shut off the vacuum cleaner immediately if the volunteer experiences any discomfort.

Explanation: This experiment provides a truly unforgettable illustration of just how powerful the air around us really is. By removing the air from inside the bag, outside air pressure will tightly envelop the plastic bag around the body, so that it molds to every contour. You will even be able to make out individual toes and fingers! When foods are vacuum packed, such as Slim Jims, a similar process is used.

Air Pressure – Experiment # 3:
WHY STRAWS ARE NEVER LONGER THAN 34 FEET

Objective: To demonstrate that air pressure can support a column of water to a height of no more than 34 feet.

Materials: • 35 – 40 foot length of narrow transparent plastic tubing (available from a hardware store)
                  • Food coloring

Safety Precautions: Do only under adult supervision. Be careful not to fall from the 35 foot height.

Procedure: 1. Draw a line around the tubing at the 34 foot mark.
                2. Find a window that is at least 34 feet above the ground.
                3. Dangle the rubber tubing down to a person on the ground. Have that person place the end of the tubing into a glass of colored water.
                4. Attempt to drink colored water through the tubing, just like you would drink water through a straw. Observe what happens.

Explanation: Atmospheric pressure can only support a column of water to a height of 33.66 feet at sea level. The air can support a column of mercury to a height of 76 cm. or 29.92 inches at sea level. The column of water that the air can support is 13.5 times higher than the column of mercury, because mercury is 13.5 times denser than water. If we had a column of air of the same diameter as that used in a barometer, and it extended to the top of the atmosphere, this air would weigh the same as 76 cm. of mercury (or 33.66 feet of water). Air pressure decreases as elevation above sea level increases – the higher the altitude, the less the air pressure. This is because the total weight of the air above you decreases as altitude increases. Changing weather conditions also affect air pressure. Barometric pressure will generally fall as inclement weather approaches. A rise in barometric pressure usually signals the advent of fair weather. So 76 cm. of mercury represents what is known as standard atmospheric pressure; in reality it will usually differ a little from this value.

When you drink water from a straw, you are not sucking water through the straw. You are simply removing the air, creating a vacuum in the straw. Air pressure pushing down on the surface of the water forces the water up the straw. Since the air can only support a column of water a little less than 34 feet high, it would be impossible to drink water out of a straw that is taller than this!

Air Pressure – Experiment # 4:
HOW TO BOIL WATER WITHOUT HEATING

Objective: To discover the effect of air pressure on the boiling point of water.

Materials:
- Vacuum winesaver (available from grocery store in the wine section)
- Empty wine bottle

Safety Precautions: None

Procedure:
1. Fill the bottle about halfway with hot water from the tap.
2. Attach the vacuum winesaver and begin removing air from the bottle.
3. Continue removing air until bubbles form in the water.
4. Remove the vacuum winesaver and allow air back into the bottle. Observe the bubbles.

Explanation: Water boils at 100° C under standard atmospheric pressure, which is 14.7 psi or 1 atm. However, under lower pressures water boils at lower temperatures. For every 1000 foot increase in altitude, the boiling point of water decreases approximately 1° C. This means that at an altitude of 5,000 feet, water would boil at about 95° C. On top of Mt. Everest, which is over 29,000 feet high, water would boil at around 71° C. At an elevation of 12 miles, your blood would boil!

Since water boils at lower temperatures at higher elevations, it takes longer to cook foods at high altitudes. This is why packages of cake mixes and other foods that require baking often come with high altitude instructions. Many people in these areas use a pressure cooker, which does not allow steam to escape. This raises the boiling point substantially, cooking foods quicker than you could under normal atmospheric conditions.

By lowering the air pressure, you are increasing the escaping tendency of water molecules. When water boils, water molecules are rapidly leaving the liquid phase and entering the gas phase. Less pressure makes it easier for these molecules to escape. In a perfect vacuum, water could boil at any temperature, even water close to 0°C. With the vacuum winesaver, a perfect vacuum is not achieved, but there is enough of a reduction in pressure to observe boiling at a temperature substantially lower than 100° C. Boiling occurs when bubbles of water vapor form within the interior of the liquid, and are forced to the top because they are less dense than the surrounding liquid.

Air Pressure – Experiment # 5:
HOW A BAROMETER WORKS

Objective: To discover how a barometer is constructed and the principle that makes it work.

Materials:
- 3 foot length of clear plastic tubing (available from hardware store)
- Snapple bottle (or equivalent)
- Food coloring
- Large beaker or basin to hold water
- Electric drill

Safety Precautions: Exercise caution when using electric drill.

Procedure:
1. In the lid of the bottle, drill a hole so that the plastic tubing can fit through snugly. Place the hole near the edge of the lid.
2. Drill another, much smaller hole on the opposite side of the lid.
3. Insert the tubing through the large hole of the lid so that it reaches the bottom of the bottle.
4. Fill a large beaker with water and add food coloring to make the water more visible.
5. Invert the empty bottle into the beaker of water so that the lid is completely immersed. The tubing should be inserted into the bottle, and the other end should curve upward out of the water.
6. Remove the air from the tubing (just like drinking from a straw), and observe what happens to the water level within the bottle.

Explanation: As the air is removed from the bottle, a region of reduced pressure is created. Less air pressure is now inside the bottle than outside. As a result, air pressure pushing down on the surface of the water forces water up into the bottle. This is the same principle by which barometers operate. When a barometer is constructed, there must be a vacuum in the tube so that air pressure can force the mercury up the tube.

Air Pressure – Experiment # 6:
THE AMAZING BALLOON

Objective: To discover that air exerts pressure.

Materials: • Balloon
  • 2-Liter bottle

Safety Precautions: None

Procedure: 1. Blow up a balloon and fasten it securely over the threads on the mouth of a 2-L bottle, keeping the balloon inflated. Predict what will happen to the balloon when you remove your fingers.
2. Remove your fingers from the balloon. Observe what happens.

Explanation: The results of this experiment are quite surprising. At first glance, it seems like the air should rush out of the balloon and into the bottle. However, this is not the case. The balloon deflates very little, if at all. Since the bottle is filled with air, the air in the balloon has nowhere to go. Any air that might escape from the balloon into the bottle is prevented from doing so by the air already in the bottle. This keeps the balloon inflated.

So why then does a balloon deflate if blown up and released? Is the room not filled with air? How does the air in the room differ from the air that is in the bottle? The air in the bottle cannot escape, but the air in the room can. When the balloon is released in the room, the air escaping from the balloon forces some of the air from the room; therefore the balloon deflates. But even a deflated balloon will have a little air left inside of it. This is because air pressure pushing back on the balloon prevents all of the air from leaving the balloon. Does the container size have an affect on the results of this experiment? Try a smaller container, and then a larger one. What happens? Why?

Air Pressure – Experiment # 7:
MAGIC WITH A DRINKING STRAW

Objective: To discover why water can remain suspended in a drinking straw, seemingly in defiance of gravity.

Materials:
- Drinking straw
- Cup of water

Safety Precautions: None

Procedure:
1. Place a drinking straw into a cup of water.
2. Place your thumb over the top.
3. Keeping your thumb over the top of the straw, lift it out from the water.
4. Observe carefully. Remove your thumb from the top of the straw. Repeat the experiment, making careful observations each time.

Explanation: This very simple experiment has been casually performed so many times that most people take it for granted that the water will stay in the straw. Yet few can actually explain why the water does not fall out. Careful observation will reveal the reason why.

When the straw is removed from the cup of water, you should notice a drop or two of water fall from the straw. Even if a drop does not fall, you will probably notice a drop hanging from the bottom. This is simply due to gravity acting on the water in the straw, pulling it downward. Yet as soon as a tiny bit of water leaves the straw, the existing air in the straw expands to fill this vacant space. The same amount of gas molecules now fill a larger space within the straw. Therefore the air in the straw will exert less pressure. This means that outside air pressure will be greater than the pressure of the air inside the straw. Therefore the water will not fall from the straw. But as soon as your thumb is removed, air rushes in to fill this region of reduced pressure, causing the water to fall from the straw, since the air pressure in the straw is now equal to air pressure outside the straw.

Air Pressure – Experiment # 8:
THE AMAZING POWER OF THE AIR

Objective: To demonstrate the power of the air.

Materials: • Electric drill
                  • 2-Liter bottle
                  • Balloon

Safety Precautions: Exercise caution when using electric drill.

Procedure: 1. Drill a small hole in the cap of a 2-Liter bottle.

2. Fill the bottle with water and invert. Water should flow out of the hole. If not, enlarge the hole.
3. Inflate a balloon and place it snugly over the cap. Predict what will happen to the flow of water when the bottle is inverted.
4. Invert the bottle. Observe what happens to the flow of water.
5. Enlarge the hole. Does this change the outcome of the experiment?

Explanation: When the bottle is inverted, water will flow out of the hole due to gravity. However, when an inflated balloon is placed over the cap and the bottle is inverted, no water will flow from the hole. Gravity is still acting on the water, but another force opposes gravity, preventing the water from leaving the bottle. This force is exerted by the air in the balloon, which prevents the water from coming out of the hole.

If the bottle is inverted without the attached balloon, is not air pressure still acting? Why doesn't this air keep the water in the bottle? How does the air around us differ from the air in the balloon? Since the balloon is inflated, the air in the balloon is under greater pressure than normal air, therefore the air within the balloon exerts a greater force than the air which surrounds us. If a deflated balloon was attached to the bottle, it would not prevent the water from leaving the bottle, since the air in the deflated balloon would exert the same pressure as the air around us.

Air Pressure – Experiment # 9:
THE UPSIDE-DOWN BALLOON IN THE BOTTLE

Objective: To witness the extraordinary effect of air pressure.

Materials:

- Ringstand
- 10 cm. diameter ring with clamp
- 8 cm. diameter ring with clamp (If ringstand and rings are not available, improvise using other materials found around the house.)
- Large pickle jar
- Matches
- Newspaper
- Duct tape
- Balloon

Safety Precautions: Perform only under adult supervision. Do in a well-ventilated area since a lot of smoke will be produced. Be careful with matches. Keep a fire extinguisher nearby.

Procedure:

1. Fill a balloon with water (and tie it off) so it rests on top of the pickle jar without falling in. The diameter of the balloon should be noticeably larger than the mouth of the jar.
2. Remove the balloon from the jar and turn the jar upside down. Place several pieces of duct tape on the bottom of the balloon (see illustration on following page), covering any part of the balloon that is not in direct contact with the water inside.
3. Place the two rings on the ringstand. The smaller ring should be about 8 cm. below the larger ring.
4. Place the water balloon upside down between the two rings. It should rest on top of the smaller ring, and extend through the larger ring, so that part of the balloon is extending through the top of the larger ring. The entire balloon should be able to slide somewhat easily completely through the top ring. Make sure the duct tape on the balloon is facing up. When the pickle jar is inverted, the balloon should make a tight seal over the mouth of the jar and the rim of the jar should rest on the top ring.
5. Loosely roll up a quarter sheet of newspaper and place it in the jar. Situate the paper so it does not fall out when the jar is inverted.

---

6. Light the paper within the jar, and just before the flame goes out, quickly invert it and place it directly over the water balloon. Make sure the mouth of the jar rests comfortably on the ring, and the balloon makes a tight seal with the mouth of the jar. Observe the behavior of the balloon.

Explanation: The balloon in the jar is a classic demonstration of air pressure. The upside down version is even more dramatic. The balloon will appear to be "sucked" up into the jar, creating an awe-inspiring spectacle.

When the fire is set inside of the jar, the air within the jar is heated. When air is heated, its molecules begin to move faster, causing them to spread farther apart. This expansion results in some air leaving the jar. When the jar is placed over the balloon, the fire goes out due to lack of oxygen. Therefore the air remaining in the jar cools. When this air cools, it exerts less pressure than before, creating a region of reduced pressure within the jar. Outside air pressure is now greater than inside air pressure. As a result, the balloon is pushed (not sucked!) into the jar by this greater outside air pressure. The fact that the balloon is pushed upward proves that air pressure is exerted in all directions, not just downward.

The duct tape is placed on the balloon to prevent the fire from popping the balloon. The part of the balloon in contact with the water will not be popped, since the water keeps the balloon cool, conducting heat away from the rubber. But any part of the balloon not in contact with the water will need to be protected with duct tape.

The partial vacuum created in the jar is sometimes erroneously attributed to the fact that oxygen in the jar is consumed by the fire. It is true that fire consumes oxygen, but the combustion of paper also produces other gases – mostly carbon dioxide and water vapor. Since these gases take the place of oxygen, the pressure decrease can only be attributed to the fact that as the air is heated in the jar, this air expands and leaves the jar.

Air Pressure – Experiment # 10:
THE JUICE BOX FOUNTAIN

Objective: To discover the effect of increasing air pressure.

Materials: • Full juice box with straw

Safety Precautions: None

Procedure: 1. Insert a straw into a full juice box.
2. Blow very hard into the straw and then immediately remove your mouth from the straw. Observe.

Explanation: Even a full juice box will contain some air above the juice. If not, it would be impossible to drink from a juice box using a straw! Contrary to popular belief, fluid is not sucked up through a straw. Instead, a vacuum is created as air is removed from the straw. Air pressure pushing down on the surface of the liquid forces fluid up the straw.

When you blow into the straw, you are forcing more air into the juice box, which can only expand slightly. Therefore, you are greatly increasing the air pressure in the box. This increased air pressure pushes down on the surface of the fluid. As a result, the juice is forced up and out of the straw, making quite a mess if you are not careful!

Air Pressure – Experiment # 11:
TOILET PAPER STREAMERS

Objective: To discover how Bernoulli's Principle operates.

Materials:

- Leaf blower
- Broomstick
- Four rolls of toilet paper

Safety Precautions: Operate leaf blower only under adult supervision.

Procedure: 1. Place four rolls of toilet paper on a broomstick. Make sure they all open in the same direction, and roll over the top away from you.
2. Have two people hold the ends of the broomstick containing the toilet paper.
3. Turn on the leaf blower and blow over the tops of the rolls of toilet paper.

Explanation: The toilet paper should fly very rapidly off the rolls, creating quite a spectacle! If pointed up into the air, the toilet paper can be made to travel quite high. This is an excellent demonstration of Bernoulli's Principle. Bernoulli's principle states that moving air exerts less pressure than still air. Since molecules of air are being forced to move in a horizontal direction, they cannot exert as great a force in the vertical direction.

By blowing air in a horizontal direction over the rolls of toilet paper, the air pressure is decreased on the tops of the rolls. As a result, the air pressure from below the rolls of toilet paper is greater. This greater air pressure acting from underneath causes the toilet paper to fly rapidly off the rolls.

Bernoulli's Principle is named after Daniel Bernoulli, a Swiss scientist of the 18th century. He made many important discoveries concerning the behavior of fluids (liquids or gases) under pressure.

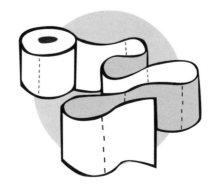

Air Pressure – Experiment # 12:
BERNOULLI'S PRINCIPLE IN ACTION

Objective: To demonstrate that moving air exerts less pressure than still air.

Materials: • Strip of paper approximately 1 inch wide by 6 inches long

Safety Precautions: None

Procedure: Holding the piece of paper directly below your bottom lip, blow strongly across the top of the paper.

Explanation: This experiment, though very simple, vividly demonstrates Bernoulli's Principle, which states that moving air exerts less pressure than still air. By blowing across the top of the paper, you are decreasing air pressure on top of the paper. Air pressure underneath the paper is now greater, so it lifts up the paper in dramatic fashion. If you have ever tried to read a book outside on a windy day, the same thing will happen. Wind blowing across the top page will reduce the pressure on top of your book, which in turn causes the greater air pressure underneath to flip the pages rapidly.

Bernoulli's Principle is sometimes referred to as the "shower curtain effect," since a shower curtain will sometimes bow inward while you are taking a shower. The movement of water in the shower creates lower air pressure inside the shower than outside, so the greater pressure from the outside pushes in the shower curtain.

Air Pressure – Experiment # 13:
LEVITATING A BEACH BALL

Objective: To demonstrate Bernoulli's Principle.

Materials:
- Leaf blower
- Beach ball

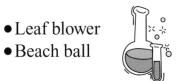

Safety Precautions: Use leaf blower only under adult supervision.

Procedure:
1. Aim the leaf blower straight up into the air. Place a beach ball in the path of the air. The ball should remain suspended in the air.
2. Gradually move the leaf blower until it makes a 45° angle with the floor. The ball should remain suspended.

Explanation: The air directly underneath the beach ball is in constant motion; therefore it exerts less pressure than the air directly above the beach ball, which is not moving. The ball is actually surrounded by still air on the top and sides, which exerts greater pressure than the air directly underneath the ball. This still air pushing in prevents the stream of air underneath from carrying the ball farther than it does.

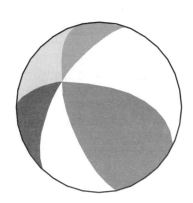

Air Pressure – Experiment # 14:
THE AMAZING WINDBAG

Objective: To discover how Bernoulli's Principle can be put to practical use.

Materials: • Two windbags (Order from FizzBang Science.) Alternately, two ski bags can be acquired from an airport.

Safety Precautions: Do not put bags over anyone's head. Keep away from small children, as the bags may pose a suffocation hazard.

Procedure: 1. Tie a knot in one end of each of two windbags, leaving the other end open.
2. Challenge a friend to a contest to see who can blow up their bag the fastest.
3. Have two assistants hold the ends of each bag so they are both horizontal.
4. You can always win this contest by holding the mouth of the bag at arm's length and blowing once directly into the bag. The entire bag will inflate in one breath!

Explanation: The windbag is a long, narrow plastic bag that is about 8 feet long and about 8 inches wide. If not available, any long, narrow bag will suffice. The bag can be blown up the old fashioned way – with a lot of huffing and puffing. But the Bernoulli way is much easier! By holding the mouth of the bag at arm's length and blowing into the bag, you set up a region of reduced pressure, since this air is moving. Moving air always exerts less pressure than still air.

Since outside air pressure is greater than air pressure at the mouth of the bag, air rushes in from the room to fill the bag much faster than if you tried to blow it up the old fashioned way. It will take a little practice to perfect this technique, but once you do, the results will amaze your friends!

Air Pressure – Experiment # 15:
THE MAGIC FUNNEL

Objective: To demonstrate Bernoulli's Principle.

Materials: • Funnel
                   • Ping-pong ball

Safety Precautions: None

Procedure: 1. Place a ping-pong ball in a funnel.
2. Blow into the funnel through the stem.
3. While blowing, slowly invert the funnel until it is upside down. The ping-pong ball will not fall out, but will remain suspended in the funnel, even when upside down!

Explanation: By blowing into the funnel, a region of lower air pressure is produced. Moving air exerts less pressure than still air.   When turned completely upside down, the ping-pong ball will not fall out of the funnel.   Since the air above the ball is moving and exerts less pressure, air pressure from underneath the ball is now greater. This prevents the ball from falling.

Bernoulli's Principle is responsible for many everyday phenomena we take for granted. Airplanes fly in part due to Bernoulli's Principle. The wings are shaped in such a way that air flowing over the top of the wing has farther to travel than wind traveling underneath the wing. As a result, air moves faster along the top of the wing than on the bottom. This creates lift, which helps to keep the airplane aloft. Frisbees glide for the same reason. Helicopters fly because the propellers create a region of lower pressure above, resulting in air pressure underneath lifting the helicopter into the air. Helicopters cannot fly at higher elevations because the air pressure is not great enough to provide lift.

Air Pressure – Experiment # 16:
THE AMAZING SPACE BAG

Objective: To demonstrate a practical use of air pressure.

Materials:
- Space Bag (available at 800-469-9044 or www.spacebag.com)
- Vacuum cleaner with hose
- Pillow

Safety Precautions: Keep the Space Bag out of reach of small children. It could pose a suffocation hazard.

Procedure:
1. Place a pillow in the Space Bag and seal tightly shut.
2. Attach the vacuum cleaner hose and remove the air from the bag.

Explanation: The remarkable Space Bag is a great way to demonstrate the incredible power of air pressure. By removing (not sucking!) the air from the bag, the air pressure within the bag is greatly reduced. Outside air pressure therefore greatly compresses the pillow within the bag. The final volume of the pillow is drastically reduced, showing how much air actually exists within a pillow. When air is allowed back into the bag, the pillow expands to its normal size. The Space Bag is marketed as a way to save space when storing pillows, blankets, or other bulky items.

Air Pressure – Experiment # 17:
THE INEFFECTIVE DRINKING STRAW

Objective: To discover how air pressure affects the operation of a drinking straw.

Materials:
- Two drinking straws
- Glass of water

Safety Precautions: None

Procedure:
1. Place a straw in your mouth with the other end in the glass of water.
2. Place a second straw in your mouth, but do not place the other end in the water.
3. Attempt to drink from the first straw. Are you successful?

Explanation: You do not actually suck liquid through a straw. Air pressure pushing on the surface of a liquid forces liquid up the straw and into your mouth. This happens when you reduce the pressure inside the straw by expanding your lungs. If atmospheric pressure is greater on the surface of the water than in the straw, then water will be forced up the straw. In order for this to happen, the air pressure in your mouth must first be reduced. By letting air into your mouth through the other straw, the pressure within your mouth can never be reduced to below atmospheric pressure. Therefore you cannot drink out of the other straw!

CHAPTER 3
GAS LAWS

A scientific law describes natural phenomena for which there has been no observed deviation. Natural laws have stood the test of time. The law of gravity always applies between any two objects that have mass. The fact that energy can neither be created nor destroyed is another law.

Gases also exhibit certain behaviors that obey certain laws. These are known as the gas laws.

Gases represent a state of matter in which the molecules are moving very rapidly, thus they always expand to fill their container. They exert pressure by constantly colliding with the walls of their container. Gases are much less dense than either liquids or solids, and are usually invisible.

Each gas law is identified by its own specific name, and is usually named after the scientist who discovered the law, or else named in honor of a scientist whose work may have helped to form the foundation on which the law is based.

This chapter is in many ways a continuation of the last, in that air pressure is often involved in discovering how a particular gas law operates . . .

Gas Laws – Experiment # 1:
BOYLE'S LAW IN A BOTTLE

Objective: To demonstrate that increasing the pressure on a gas will decrease its volume.

Materials:

- Balloon
- Straw
- Bottle
- Fizz-Keeper (available from grocery or department store)

Safety Precautions: Wear safety goggles. To avoid overpressurizing the bottle, do not pump up the bottle with the Fizz-Keeper more than 100 times. When releasing the pressure, unscrew the Fizz-Keeper slowly from the bottle. Never aim the Fizz-Keeper at another person, and never place your face directly over the Fizz-Keeper, especially when unscrewing it from the bottle. Never use the Fizz-Keeper on a glass bottle.

Procedure:

1. Blow up a balloon inside of a 2-Liter bottle and tie it off. The balloon can be of any size. You must insert a straw next to your balloon as you blow it up inside of the bottle.
2. Now screw on the Fizz-Keeper and pump up the bottle with air. Do not pump the Fizz-Keeper more than 100 times. Observe.
3. Unscrew the Fizz-Keeper slowly from the bottle and watch what happens.

Explanation: This experiment is a perfect illustration of Boyle's Law, which states that as the pressure on a gas increases, its volume decreases. As the bottle fills with more air, more molecules collide with the outside walls of the balloon, causing the balloon to shrink.

    As for the expansion in volume when the Fizz-Keeper is released, Boyle's Law also states that as the pressure exerted on a gas decreases, its volume increases. As the compressed air within the bottle escapes, the pressure on the balloon decreases. This causes the balloon to expand to its original volume. Notice that the balloon does not expand indefinitely, however. Since atmospheric pressure is still being exerted on the balloon at a pressure of about 14.7 lbs. per square inch (psi), the volume of the balloon is kept in check.

Gas Laws – Experiment # 2
BOYLE'S LAW IN A BOTTLE: PART 2

Objective: To measure the decrease in the volume of a gas due to an increase in pressure.

Materials:

- Plastic syringe (without needle – available from a drug store)
- Candle
- Matches
- 2-Liter bottle
- Fizz-Keeper

Safety Precautions: Exercise caution when lighting candle. Do only under adult supervision. Wear safety goggles. To avoid overpressurizing the bottle, do not pump up the bottle with the Fizz-Keeper more than 100 times. When releasing the pressure, unscrew the Fizz-Keeper slowly from the bottle. Never aim the Fizz-Keeper at another person, and never place your face directly over the Fizz-Keeper, especially when unscrewing it from the bottle. Never use the Fizz-Keeper on a glass bottle.

Procedure:
1. Open the syringe to the highest measured increment and then melt the end shut over a candle flame. Place the syringe in the bottle.
2. Attach the Fizz-Keeper and pump up the bottle. Do not pump the Fizz-Keeper more than 100 times. Observe.

Explanation: As the bottle is pumped full of air, the syringe will become depressed because the air pressure within the bottle is increasing. When the Fizz-Keeper is unscrewed, the air pressure within the bottle is decreased, and the air in the syringe will expand to its original volume. Boyle's Law states that pressure and volume are inversely proportional. So if the initial volume of the air in the syringe was 4 cubic centimeters (cc), we can easily predict what pressure will be required to depress the syringe to a volume of 2 cc. If we assume initial air pressure to be 1 atmosphere (atm), which is the standard atmospheric pressure at sea level, then a pressure of 2 atm will reduce the volume of the air in the syringe by one-half. If the air in the syringe were to attain a volume of 1 cc, then this would mean 4 atm of pressure were being exerted. You can easily graph this data by recording the volume after every 20 pumps with the Fizz-Keeper.

Is there any danger of blowing up the bottle to the point where it would burst? Hardly. At the bottling plant, the typical pressure that exists within a 2-Liter bottle of soda is about 60 psi. This is over four times greater than atmospheric pressure! This pressure would be very difficult to attain using just a Fizz-Keeper.

Gas Laws – Experiment # 3:
SODA IN A VACUUM

Objective: To determine the effect of reduced pressure on the bubbles within a bottle of soda.

Materials:
- Vacuum winesaver pump (available in the wine section of the grocery store)
- Empty glass wine bottle
- Soda

Procedure:
1. Fill the wine bottle about halfway with soda.
2. Attach the vacuum pump to the bottle and pump to remove the air.
3. Observe the size of the bubbles.

Explanation: The vacuum winesaver can be purchased for just a few dollars. It is a great way to form a vacuum within a bottle. It has the exact opposite effect as the Fizz-Keeper. The Fizz-Keeper increases the pressure in the bottle, whereas the vacuum pump reduces the pressure. Each also affects the bubbles differently. The Fizz-Keeper reduces the size of the bubbles, but the vacuum pump causes the bubbles to grow much larger. By reducing the air pressure above the bubbles, they are free to expand to a much larger size. You will even observe bubbles forming from within the solution, where it appeared there were no bubbles previously. Numerous microscopic bubbles are in the solution, but only grow to visible size when the pressure above them is reduced.

Gas Laws – Experiment # 4:
A POTATO LAUNCHER

Objective: To use compressed air to launch a potato.

Materials:

- Piece of sturdy plastic tubing 2 – 3 feet in length (available from an aquarium dealer)
- Piece of PVC pipe about one foot longer than plastic tubing, that can easily slide into the plastic tubing. Diameter of PVC pipe should only be slightly less than that of the plastic tubing (Half-inch PVC pipe should work well with most aquarium tubes)
- T-shaped PVC pipe connector
- PVC cement
- Potatoes
- Clay

Safety Precautions: Do only under adult supervision. Do not aim at people.

Procedure:

1. Using PVC cement, attach the T-shaped connector to the end of the PVC pipe. This will be the handle to your plunger.
2. Plug the other end of the PVC pipe with clay, or temporarily with a piece of potato.
3. Place the plastic tubing over a potato and press down firmly until it has completely passed through the potato. You should now have a potato plug in the end of the plastic tube.
4. Insert the plunger into the plastic tube and launch the potato plug. It will not go very far.
5. Insert another plug into the end of the plastic tube, and using the plunger, push it about a third of the way down the tube.
6. Now place another plug in the opposite end of the tube. About two-thirds of the tube should now be between the two plugs.
7. Now launch the potato plug using the plunger. It should go much farther.

Explanation: The first time you launched the potato plug, it probably was a big disappointment. It did not travel far because you were only physically expelling the plug with the plunger. The second time it should have traveled much farther because you were using the power of compressed air to your advantage. When there is a column of air between the two plugs, this air becomes compressed when the plunger is pushed into the tube. As a result of being compressed, this air exerts a much greater pressure, great enough to force the plug out of the tube at a high velocity. The plug left the tube without the other plug coming in contact with it due to the pressure this column of compressed air was exerting. This experiment provides verification of Boyle's Law, which states that as the volume of a gas is decreased, its pressure increases. This increase in pressure of the air in the tube forced the potato plug from the tube.

Gas Laws – Experiment # 5:
THE MAGIC BALLOON

Objective: To demonstrate that air exerts more pressure when it is compressed, and less pressure when it expands.

Materials:
- 2-Liter bottle
- Balloon
- Nail

Safety Precautions: None

Procedure:
1. Fill a 2-Liter bottle to the brim with water.
2. Inflate a balloon and attach it to the mouth of the bottle. It should stay inflated.
3. With a nail, poke a small hole in the side of the bottle near the base. Water will begin to flow from the hole.
4. Measure the distance the water travels initially as compared to how far it travels when the water level has gone down.
5. Give the balloon an occasional squeeze. Note how this affects the distance the water travels from the hole.
6. Observe the balloon when the water level reaches the hole.
7. Refill the bottle with water and measure how far the water travels without a balloon attached. Compare this distance with how far the water travels with a balloon attached.
8. Place the cap on the bottle. How does this affect the distance the water travels?

Explanation: The air in the balloon pushes against the surface of the water, forcing water out of the hole. The water should travel farther with the balloon attached than without, which shows that the air in the balloon exerts more pressure than does the atmosphere. When the cap is placed on the bottle, hardly any water at all will flow from the hole, since we have prevented the weight of the atmosphere from pushing down on the surface of the water. Water only flows through the hole when pressure is applied to its surface. As soon as the water level reaches the hole, the balloon will deflate since the air can now escape.

Squeezing the balloon should cause water to travel farther out of the hole. This is because squeezing the balloon compresses the air inside of the bottle, which causes it to exert more pressure. Boyle's Law states that as the volume of a gas is decreased, its pressure increases. By squeezing the balloon and decreasing its volume, it is able to exert a greater pressure, forcing the water to travel a greater distance out of the hole.

As the water level in the bottle decreases, the water will not travel as far out of the hole. This is primarily because as the water level decreases, there is less pressure exerted by the water itself. Another reason is because as the air in the balloon fills the bottle, it occupies a greater volume, causing the air to exert less pressure. Boyle's Law states that as a gas expands under constant temperature, it exerts less pressure. If a gas is compressed, it exerts more pressure.

Gas Laws – Experiment # 6:
THE MAGIC BALLOON: PART 2

Objective: To demonstrate that air exerts more pressure when it is compressed, and less pressure when it is allowed to expand.

Materials:
- 2-Liter bottle
- Balloon
- Nail

Safety Precautions: None

Procedure:
1. Fill a 2-Liter bottle to the brim with water.
2. Place a deflated balloon over the mouth of the bottle.
3. Poke a small hole in the side of the bottle, near the base, with a nail.
4. Observe the behavior of the balloon.
5. Lift the balloon up into the air and pull up on it several times until it gets pushed down into the bottle. Observe the distance the water travels through the hole as you are doing this.
6. Once the balloon is inside the bottle and completely inverted, blow air into it to inflate it. Observe the distance the water travels through the hole as you do this. You can also poke it with your finger to observe the same effect.
7. Give the bottle a good squeeze. Observe the balloon.

Explanation: When the deflated balloon is placed over the bottle, air pressure acting on it pushes it into the bottle. This is because any water that leaves through the hole creates a vacuum in the space above the water. Air can thus enter the space that the water formerly occupied. Since air pressure is greater on the outside of the bottle than on the inside, the balloon is pushed (not sucked!) into the bottle. However, there is a little air still left in the bottle, because it is never possible to remove all of the air, and a little air was likely present in the bottle from the beginning.

Initially, very little water will flow out of the hole, since there is only a small amount of air in the space above the water. By pulling up on the balloon, the water flow will immediately cease, since the air in the bottle will expand to fill a greater volume, causing it to exert less pressure. When the balloon is allowed to snap back into the bottle, it momentarily compresses the air in the bottle, causing it to exert more pressure and force the water out of the hole.

When air is blown into the inverted balloon, it serves to compress the air already in the bottle, causing it to exert a greater pressure and thus force water out of the hole. The same effect can be observed by poking at the balloon.

If the bottle itself is squeezed, the balloon will inflate and be forced out of the bottle. Water will also be forced out of the hole. This is another way to compress the air in the bottle. By reducing its volume, the air exerts a greater pressure, causing the balloon to inflate. Water is also forced out of the hole. This experiment serves as a good validation of Boyle's Law, which states that as the volume of a gas decreases, its pressure increases, and vice versa. In other words the volume and pressure of a gas are inversely proportional.

Gas Laws – Experiment # 7:
CAN YOU BLOW A PIECE OF PAPER INTO A BOTTLE?

Objective: To discover that as air is compressed, its pressure increases.

Materials:
- Piece of paper
- Empty 2-Liter bottle

Safety Precautions: None

Procedure:
1. Wad up a small piece of paper to about the size of a pea.
2. Place a 2-L bottle on its side on a table. Place the paper on the inside rim of the bottle.
3. Kneel down so that your mouth is level with the bottle.
4. Try to blow the wad of paper into the bottle. It may be more difficult than it sounds!

Explanation: This little experiment may provide you with a great way to make some money if you bet your friends that they cannot blow the piece of paper into the bottle. When attempted, the piece of paper usually flies back and hits you in the face! Why is such a seemingly simple task so difficult to perform? The answer has to do with Boyle's Law, which states that as the volume of a gas decreases, its pressure increases. By blowing into the bottle, you are forcing the air into the bottle to temporarily occupy a smaller space. This will cause the pressure of that gas to increase. Since the bottle has an opening, this increase in pressure is only momentary, and the excess air is immediately forced back out, taking the piece of paper with it!

You can blow the piece of paper into the bottle by blowing softly, which only increases the pressure a tiny amount, so the paper can easily be blown into the bottle.

Gas Laws – Experiment # 8:
THE EXPANDING PING-PONG BALL

Objective: To observe the effects of heating air in an enclosed space.

Materials:

- Beaker or microwaveable glassware
- Ping-pong ball
- Potholder
- Microwave oven

Safety Precautions: Use microwave oven only under adult supervision. Water in beaker will be boiling when finished – exercise caution.

Procedure:

1. Using your thumb, make an indentation in a ping-pong ball.
2. Place this indented ping-pong ball into a beaker nearly full with water.
3. Turn on the microwave for several minutes.
4. Using a potholder, remove the beaker. Be careful, because the water will be very hot!   Remove the ping-pong ball. Observe.

Explanation: As the ping-pong ball is heated, the air inside will be heated as well. As the molecules of air are heated, they will begin moving faster. As they move faster, they will collide more frequently with the inside walls of the ping-pong ball. This will cause the ping-pong ball to expand back to its original shape and volume. This is in accordance with Charles' Law, which states that as the temperature of a gas increases, its volume increases.

Gas Laws – Experiment # 9:
SHRINKING A STYROFOAM CUP

Objective: To observe the effects of heat and pressure on a Styrofoam cup.

Materials:

- Pressure cooker
- Stove
- Styrofoam cup

Safety Precautions: Do only under adult supervision. Never operate a pressure cooker without safety release valve, and never operate a pressure cooker without a thorough knowledge of its operation. Never attempt to open a pressure cooker while it is hot. Improper use of the pressure cooker can result in serious injury.

Procedure:

1. Place about an inch of water in the pressure cooker, and place within a Styrofoam cup open end down. If you want, you can draw a design or write on the cup first.
2. Replace the lid with the pressure relief valve and heat on the stove for 10 minutes.
3. Remove from heat and allow to sit for 1 hour before opening.
4. Open and remove the cup. Observe. The time of heating may need to be adjusted to allow for best results.

Explanation: The results of this experiment are astonishing. The Styrofoam cup shrinks to an amazingly small size, yet is a perfect replica in every way of an undisturbed cup! Even the words written on the cup will be shrunk to perfect proportions. This incredible effect is due to the fact that Styrofoam cups are blown up with gas, and when the gas diffuses out, the spaces fill up with air. This greatly enhances its insulating ability. The volume of this air is greatly reduced by the high pressures within the pressure cooker. As a result, much of this air is forced out, causing the cup to shrink to a much smaller size.

Pressure cookers work by not allowing steam to escape, which builds up to a tremendous pressure. Water thus boils at a temperature much higher than 100°C. As a result, foods can cook much faster. Pressure cookers are especially

useful for cooking at high altitudes, where the boiling point of water is lower due to less air pressure. A combination of high pressure and intense heat shrinks the Styrofoam cups. The same effect has been observed when Styrofoam cups are submerged in the depths of the ocean. The intense pressure of the water compresses the air in the cup and drives it out. This is verification of Boyle's Law, since an increase in pressure results in a decrease in volume.

Gas Laws – Experiment # 10
REDUCING AIR PRESSURE BY RUSTING

Objective: To discover that the rusting of iron removes oxygen from the air, lowering its pressure.

Materials:
- Steel wool
- Graduated cylinder or tennis ball can
- Aluminum pie pan

Safety Precautions: None

Procedure:
1. Thoroughly wet a piece of steel wool with water and stuff into the bottom of the graduated cylinder. It should stay firmly in place when the cylinder is inverted.
2. Place the inverted cylinder into an aluminum pie pan filled with water. Note the water level in the cylinder. Leave undisturbed for 24 hours.
3. After 24 hours, the water level in the cylinder should have risen considerably.

Explanation: The steel wool will begin to rust because it is wet. Rusting is an oxidation reaction that involves the combination of iron with oxygen. The presence of water will speed the reaction along. The balanced chemical equation is as follows:

$$4Fe_{(s)} + 3O_{2(g)} \longrightarrow 2Fe_2O_{3(s)}$$

Since rusting involves reacting with oxygen gas, the amount of oxygen in the cylinder is decreased. This causes the total air pressure in the cylinder to decrease. Air is 21% oxygen, so if all the oxygen in the cylinder was removed, the air pressure would decrease from 1 atmosphere (atm) to .79 atm. Since outside air pressure is greater, there will be greater pressure from outside the cylinder than from within it. As a result, air pressure from the outside pushing down on the water forces the water up into the cylinder.

The air in the cylinder is now compressed, and compressed air exerts a greater pressure. The water in the cylinder will stop rising when the pressure within the cylinder is equivalent to the pressure outside the cylinder. This is verification of Boyle's Law, since by decreasing the volume of the air in the cylinder we are increasing its pressure, until the pressure inside the cylinder is equal to atmospheric pressure.

CHAPTER 4
PHASE CHANGES

The three most common phases of matter – gases, liquids, and solids – often change from one to the other.

Freezing is the change from a liquid to a solid.
Melting is the change from a solid to a liquid.
Boiling is the rapid change from a liquid to a gas.
Evaporation is the gradual change from a liquid to a vapor.
Condensation is the change from a gas to a liquid.
Sublimation is the change from a solid directly to a gas.
Deposition is the change from a gas directly to a solid.

In this chapter, we will explore the fascinating world of phase changes . . .

Phase Changes – Experiment # 1:
FREEZING POINT DEPRESSION

Objective: To discover the effect on temperature when antifreeze is added to snow.

Materials:

- Antifreeze
- Snow (crushed ice can be substituted if snow is not available)
- Plastic cup
- Thermometer

Safety Precautions: Perform only under adult supervision. Antifreeze contains ethylene glycol, which can be fatal if swallowed.

Procedure:

1. Fill a cup with snow and record its temperature.
2. Add antifreeze a little at a time, and stir, until the snow has melted. Record the final temperature.

Explanation: Antifreeze is very effective at melting snow. The active ingredient in antifreeze is ethylene glycol, which is soluble in water. Antifreeze melts ice by breaking apart the hydrogen bonds that join together neighboring water molecules. These molecules make up the hexagonal crystal lattice structure of ice. Melting is an endothermic process, which means that a solid must absorb energy from its surroundings in order to occur. Melting involves breaking bonds, which requires energy. This energy comes from the surroundings. Therefore the temperature of the snow drops considerably after it is melted by the antifreeze.

The temperature of the snow should have started out at approximately 0°C, and then ended up at approximately -20°C. The antifreeze greatly depresses the freezing point of the water, which is why it is put into car radiators. If antifreeze was not added to the radiator of your car in the wintertime, the fluid within the radiator could freeze up when the temperature drops. Since water expands when it freezes, a car can suffer serious engine damage if the radiator fluid freezes.

Phase Changes – Experiment # 2:
WHAT IS THE WHITE CLOUD ABOVE A WHISTLING TEAKETTLE?

Objective: To demonstrate that steam is invisible.

Materials:

- Teakettle
- Stove
- Propane torch

Safety Precautions: Do this experiment only under adult supervision. Exercise caution when boiling water and using a propane torch.

Procedure:
1. Heat water to boiling in teakettle.
2. Using the propane torch, heat the white cloud coming from the teakettle. Observe.

Explanation: The teakettle whistles due to steam passing through the small opening in the lid. As water boils, it rapidly changes from a liquid to a gas. Under normal atmospheric conditions, this occurs at 100°C. As soon as the steam comes into contact with the cold air, which is much cooler than 100°C, it condenses back into liquid water. So the white cloud above a teakettle is not steam, but actually tiny drops of liquid water. Steam is always invisible. If you look closely, you can see that it is clear for about an inch or so above the spout of a whistling teakettle. This is where steam is coming out of the hole. It has not yet condensed into liquid water. By heating the white cloud with a propane torch, it too will become invisible. This is because we are boiling the cloud of tiny water droplets, thus turning them back into invisible steam.

Phase Changes – Experiment # 3:
BUTANE IN A BAG

Objective: To observe liquid, solid, and gaseous butane in the same container.

Materials:
- Can of butane (available at grocery store)
- Quart freezer bag

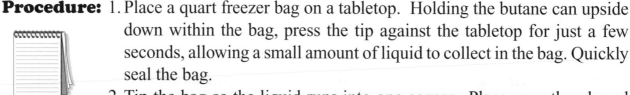

Safety Precautions: Do only under adult supervision. Wear safety goggles. Read all warning labels on can before proceeding. Under no circumstances should butane vapors be inhaled. Inhalation of vapors can be fatal. Butane is very flammable – keep away from all flames. Do not allow liquid butane to come into contact with skin. Frostbite may result.

Procedure:
1. Place a quart freezer bag on a tabletop. Holding the butane can upside down within the bag, press the tip against the tabletop for just a few seconds, allowing a small amount of liquid to collect in the bag. Quickly seal the bag.
2. Tip the bag so the liquid runs into one corner. Place your thumb and forefinger around the bag surrounding the liquid. Observe.
3. If the bag expands to the point where it looks like it will pop, carefully open the bag, being careful not to inhale the contents or bring them near an open flame.

Explanation: Butane is a hydrocarbon with the formula C_4H_{10}. It exists as a gas at room temperature, but if put under pressure it will liquefy. It is used in butane lighters. Some lighters contain a little window that allows you to view the butane level. You can clearly see that it is a liquid. In the space above the liquid is butane gas, which exists in equilibrium with the liquid below it. Whenever a lighter is used, some of this gas escapes and is burned.

   In the can, butane also exists as a liquid, which you can hear if the can is shaken. Above the liquid in the can is a gas, which can be released if the can is held upright and the tip pressed against the bottom of a tabletop. When held upside down, however, the more dense liquid will be released.

   Under normal atmospheric pressure, butane boils at 0°C. So as soon as this liquid escapes from its high pressure environment within the can, it immediately begins to boil. However, since boiling is an endothermic (heat absorbing) process, it removes energy from its surroundings. So much energy is removed that the temperature of the butane is brought below its boiling point of 0°C, so it condenses back into a liquid. You can also see chunks of solid butane within the liquid. Butane freezes at -138°C. This temperature is cold enough to cause frostbite if it comes in contact with your skin.

When you place your fingers on the outside of the bag, you can immediately see the butane boil very vigorously. The heat from your fingers is far greater than the boiling point of the substance. In a short time, the solid butane will melt and all the liquid will boil. The bag will noticeably expand as it fills with butane gas.

Phase Changes – Experiment # 4:
THE EVAPORATION RACE

Objective: To discover what factors affect the rate of evaporation of different liquids.

Materials:

- Ethyl alcohol (available in hardware store as denatured alcohol)
- Methyl alcohol (available in drug store)
- Acetone (available in hardware store or as fingernail polish remover)
- Paint thinner (contains hexane)
- Vegetable oil
- Cotton balls

Safety Precautions: Perform only under adult supervision. Wear safety goggles. All substances used (except vegetable oil) are toxic if ingested, give off harmful fumes, and are flammable. Keep away from flames. Do outdoors or in a well-ventilated area. Do not inhale vapors. Do not allow any substance to come into contact with your skin.

Procedure: Using cotton balls, dab a small amount of each of the above substances, as well as water, side by side on either a tabletop or a chalkboard. Try to use the same amount of each substance. Which evaporates the fastest?

Explanation: The rate of evaporation of a substance is determined by two factors: the strength of the intermolecular bonds and the molecular mass. The paint thinner, which contains hexane, will probably evaporate the fastest. This is because hexane (C_6H_{14}) is very nonpolar. Nonpolar substances generally have weak intermolecular bonds. (A nonpolar substance will not mix with water, which is polar.) Nonpolar substances have a very weak attraction between molecules, which means they can easily escape into the vapor phase. As a result, they evaporate quickly. Substances with a high rate of evaporation are termed volatile. Volatile substances tend to have a strong odor and are often flammable.

Acetone (CH_3COCH_3) will most likely evaporate next. Acetone is more polar than hexane. As a result it will evaporate less quickly. Its intermolecular bonds are stronger than those of hexane.

The methyl alcohol (CH_3OH) will evaporate quicker than the ethyl alcohol (C_2H_5OH) even though methyl alcohol is more polar than ethyl. This is due to another factor that affects the rate of evaporation – molecular mass. Since methyl alcohol has a smaller molecular mass (32 amu) than ethyl alcohol (46 amu), it evaporates more quickly. The heavier the molecule, the more energy it must absorb in order for it to break free from the liquid phase and enter the vapor phase. Substances composed of lighter molecules require less energy to evaporate.

Water will most likely evaporate next. Even though water molecules have a relatively small atomic mass (18 amu), they are very polar, so they require more energy to evaporate than do the nonpolar substances, even though these nonpolar substances may be heavier.

Finally, the oil will evaporate the slowest. Even though it is nonpolar, it has a very high molecular mass, causing it to have an extremely low rate of evaporation. It would definitely be the least volatile of all the substances tested.

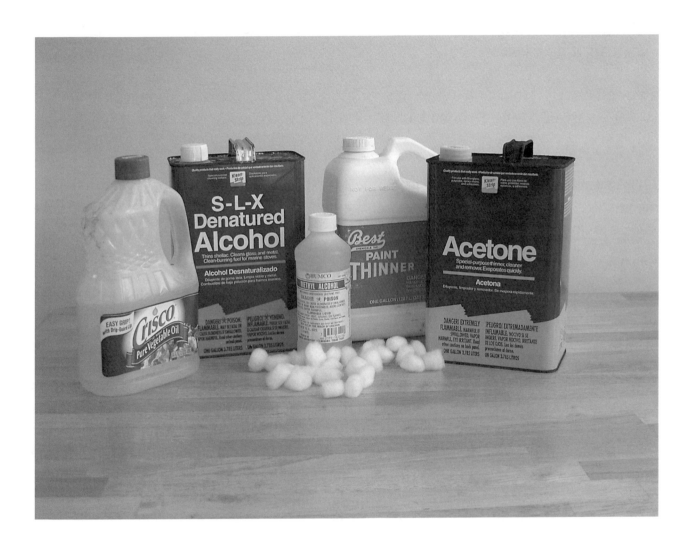

Phase Changes – Experiment # 5:
WHICH PHASE CHANGES ARE ENDOTHERMIC?

Objective: To discover which phase changes absorb energy.

Materials: • Ice cube
    • Isopropyl rubbing alcohol
    • Cotton ball

Safety Precautions: Perform only under adult supervision. Isopropyl alcohol is very toxic if ingested.

Procedure: 1. Hold an ice cube in your hand for a few seconds. What happens?
        2. Using a cotton ball, place a little rubbing alcohol on your wrist. What happens?

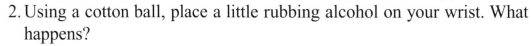

Explanation: This very simple experiment can be used to illustrate some very important chemistry – namely the relationship between phase changes and energy. The ice cube makes your hand feel cold because melting is an endothermic process. The ice absorbs energy from its surroundings. In this case, the surroundings are your hand, which releases energy to the ice cube. Anytime bonds are broken, such as when ice melts, energy must be absorbed. Putting ice in drinks makes them cold. As ice melts, it absorbs energy from the drink, making it colder.

The rubbing alcohol will also make your skin feel very cold, due to its quick rate of evaporation. Evaporation is also an endothermic process, since bonds are broken as substances go from a liquid to a vapor. As the alcohol evaporates, it removes energy from your skin, making you feel cooler. Your body perspires when you get hot for the same reason. As this perspiration evaporates, it cools your body.

Since melting and evaporation are both endothermic, the reverse processes – freezing and condensation – are exothermic. In other words, these phase changes release heat. Steam burns are very painful because when steam condenses on your skin it releases a tremendous amount of energy. If fruit growers want to protect their fruit during a frost, they will spray the fruit with water. As the water freezes around the fruit, it releases energy, keeping the fruit warm. This only works because freezing is an exothermic process.

CHAPTER 5
PROPERTIES
OF LIQUIDS

Liquids are unique in that they share some common properties that are quite different from gases and solids.

Liquids have a definite volume, but not a definite shape. They do not expand to fill their containers like gases do, but they do assume the shape of their container.

In this chapter, water plays an important part. We will also do some experiments with oil, which is the polar opposite of water. We will also explore surface tension, take a look at viscosity, and make a tornado . . .

Properties of Liquids – Experiment # 1:
TIE-DYED MILK

Objective: To discover the effect of detergent on the surface tension of a liquid.

Materials:

- Transparent plastic cup
- Whole milk
- Food coloring
- Liquid dish detergent
- Toothpick

Safety Precautions: None

Procedure:
1. Fill the cup with whole milk.
2. Place several drops each of blue, red, yellow, and green food coloring on the surface of the milk.
3. Wait several minutes until the colors have diffused across the entire surface of the milk. Do not stir or disturb in any way.
4. With the toothpick, carefully place one drop of liquid dish detergent in the center of the surface of the milk. Do not stir or disturb in any way. Observe.
5. After a few minutes, add another drop or so of dish detergent. Observe.

Explanation: A beautiful tie-dyed effect is created when the dish detergent is added to the milk and food coloring. Food coloring is actually denser than milk, but floats due to the milk's surface tension. This surface tension prevents much of the food coloring from sinking. Surface tension is due to strong intermolecular attractions between the molecules of a liquid, which creates something akin to a "skin" on the surface of the liquid.

Dish detergent is an emulsifying agent, which enables it to effectively remove dirt and grease. An emulsifying agent works because it contains both a polar and a non-polar end. The polar end contains both a positive and a negative charge, while the non-polar end does not. When added to milk, the polar end of the detergent molecules will bond to the water molecules, breaking apart the intermolecular bonds between adjacent water molecules. The nonpolar end of the detergent molecules will bond to the molecules of fat. As a result, the surface tension of the milk is destroyed. This causes the food coloring to disperse in all directions, creating the beautiful tie-dyed effect.

Properties of Liquids – Experiment # 2:
EXAMINING SURFACE TENSION

Objective: To discover how surface tension operates.

Materials:
- Static Duster (available in department stores) or equivalent
- Large transparent bowl or aquarium

Safety Precautions: None

Procedure:
1. Submerge the Static Duster underwater. Observe the bristles.
2. Remove the Static Duster from the water. Observe the bristles.

Explanation: This simple yet profound experiment clearly illustrates how surface tension operates. Underwater, the bristles are pulled in all directions because they absorb water, which is attracted by adjacent water molecules that completely surround the bristles. Therefore, the bristles spread out evenly. No surface tension acts on the bristles here, because water is acting on the bristles from every direction. This same effect can be observed underwater with a paintbrush, a mophead, or the hair on your head.

When removed from the water, the bristles become matted together, because now no water molecules pull from the outside. The only attraction is from water molecules on the surface of the bristles attracting one another. Surface tension clearly exists in this case due to unbalanced forces. In the same way, surface tension exists on the surface of a liquid because there are no forces acting upward, only downward from the body of the fluid itself. If you pick any point below the surface of a body of a liquid, surface tension would not exist because water molecules at that point exert forces from every direction. Surface tension, as the name implies, is a surface phenomenon only.

Properties of Liquids – Experiment # 3:
COMPARING THE VISCOSITY OF DIFFERENT LIQUIDS

Objective: To compare the relative viscosity of different liquids.

Materials: • One liter each of: alcohol, vegetable oil, honey, and water
   • Four transparent 1-L bottles
   • Four steel ball bearings or marbles

Safety Precautions: Do only under adult supervision. Alcohol is poisonous if ingested.

Procedure: 1. Fill the four bottles with the above four substances, respectively. Label each accordingly.
   2. Place a ball bearing or marble in each, and replace the cap on each bottle. Make sure each bottle is tightly capped.
   3. With the help of a partner, invert all four bottles simultaneously.
   4. Note the rate of fall of each ball bearing.

Explanation: Viscosity is defined as a liquid's resistance to flow. The faster the ball bearing falls through a liquid, the less viscous is the liquid. The slower the ball bearing falls, the more viscous is the liquid. It is important that viscosity not be confused with density. Oil is less dense than water, yet oil is more viscous. Whole milk is more viscous than skim milk, because whole milk has more fat. However, whole milk is less dense than skim milk because fat is less dense than water.

Properties of Liquids – Experiment # 4:
DOES TEMPERATURE AFFECT VISCOSITY?

Objective: To discover how temperature affects the viscosity of a liquid.

Materials: • One Liter of honey
              • Two transparent half-Liter bottles

Safety Precautions: Perform only under adult supervision. After heating, the honey will be very hot – be careful not to burn yourself.

Procedure:
1. Place a half-Liter of honey in the refrigerator overnight.
2. Heat another half-Liter of honey in the microwave oven for 1 – 2 minutes. It should be fairly hot, but not boiling.
3. Pour both in separate half-Liter bottles, and place a ball bearing in each.
4. Invert both bottles simultaneously and note the rate of fall of the ball bearings.

Explanation: The honey that was heated should be much less viscous than the honey that was placed in the refrigerator overnight. Viscosity refers to a liquid's resistance to flow. The slower a liquid flows, the more viscous the liquid. As liquids are heated, their molecules move faster, causing intermolecular bonds between the molecules to become weaker. As a result, these weaker bonds lead to a quicker flow rate. Most liquids become less viscous on heating, and more viscous upon cooling. For this reason, the ball bearing should have fallen more slowly in the bottle of cold honey than in the bottle of hot honey.

Properties of Liquids – Experiment # 5:
VISCOSITY OF MOTOR OILS

Objective: To discover the effect of increasing viscosity on different types of motor oils.

Materials:
- One quart each of these grades of motor oil: 5W-30, 10W-40 20W-50, 80W-90 (gear oil)
- Four identical funnels
- Four empty 2-Liter bottles

Safety Precautions: Motor oil is poisonous. Perform this experiment only under adult supervision. Be careful not to spill any motor oil, as it is difficult to clean up.

Procedure:
1. Label each bottle with a different grade of motor oil.
2. Place a funnel on top of each bottle.
3. Using four people, pour each of the four types of motor oil simultaneously into their respective bottles.
4. Note the order in which each funnel empties.

Explanation: Each of the four types of motor oil used in this experiment has a different viscosity, as indicated by the number or grade on the label. Viscosity is defined as resistance to flow. A liquid that is thick, such as molasses or honey, is more viscous than a substance that flows easily, such as water. The old saying "slower than molasses in January" refers to the fact that as liquids get colder, they become more viscous.

The motor oils used in this experiment are multigrade motor oils, meaning they undergo a range of viscosity ratings as they are heated. The first number refers to the viscosity rating when the engine is cold. The "W" refers to winter, or simply a cold engine. It does not refer to weight, as is sometimes erroneously believed. The actual weight of motor oil does not change in your engine, although its viscosity certainly does.

In the experiment performed above all of the oils are cold (relative to a hot engine), so we will look at the first number only. The oil that flowed the most quickly should have been the 5W-30, followed by the 10W-30, 20W-50, and then the 80W-90. By examining the first numbers only for each grade of oil, it is obvious that the higher the number, the greater is the viscosity of the oil. The 5W-30 oil should flow much more quickly than the 80W-90 oil. The less viscous oils are more commonly used in the winter months when the temperatures are very cold. Since viscosity is affected by temperature, an oil that is too viscous may make it more difficult for an engine to turn over in the winter. If it is too thick, it also may not provide adequate protection for engine parts before the oil has a chance to warm up, as opposed to a less viscous oil that can flow more freely. The

80W-90 oil is so thick it cannot be used in engines, but is used for the transmissions of standard shift vehicles. In the winter, a car may require a 5W-30 oil, but in the summer a 10W-30 oil could be substituted. Some smaller engines that operate under high RPMs may require a 20W-50 oil. Since this oil is more viscous, it provides better lubrication to rapidly moving engine parts.

The second number of a multigrade oil refers to the viscosity when the engine is hot. Anytime the temperature of a liquid increases, its viscosity decreases. In other words, hotter oils flow easier. So the second number of a multigrade oil can only be compared to the viscosity of another oil that is also hot. For example, a 5W-30 oil will be less viscous when hot than will a 10W-40 oil. We know this by comparing the "30" and "40." But it must be stressed that when hot, all oils are less viscous than when cold. If you change the oil in your car when the engine is hot, it will be much less viscous than when cold. Perhaps a more accurate way of expressing the viscosity of oil would be to express 10W-40 as 10W-.40 and 20W-50 as 20W-.50. This would make it clear that viscosity decreases as temperature increases, but also that when hot, the 20W-50 is more viscous than the 10W-40.

Properties of Liquids – Experiment # 6:
TORNADO IN A BOTTLE

Objective: To create a miniature tornado in a bottle.

Materials: • Tall baby food jar (or equivalent)
                 • Liquid dishwashing detergent

Safety Precautions: None

Procedure: 1. Fill the jar nearly to the top with water. Leave a little space at the top.
2. Add only 2 drops of liquid dishwashing detergent. Replace the lid.
3. Grasping the jar by the top, use your wrist to make a quick swirling motion.
4. Stop moving the jar. Observe.

Explanation: The miniature tornado you just constructed is similar to the commercial variety that can be purchased for several dollars. You have actually created a vortex in a bottle. By being swirled, the water is forced to the outside due to the inertia of the water, which would continue to travel in a straight line if there was no force to stop it. Clothes in a washing machine will be stuck to the walls of the drum after going through the spin cycle for the same reason. A centrifuge that separates substances into layers utilizes this same principle. These phenomena are sometimes erroneously attributed to centrifugal force, which is a fictitious force supposedly exerted on objects in circular motion. In the miniature tornado you constructed, since the more dense water is forced to the outside, the air is trapped on the inside.

The purpose of the detergent is to lower the surface tension of the water. Water molecules tend to stick to one another very well because they are strongly polar. The detergent molecules get in between these water molecules, prying them apart from one another. This tends to drastically lower water's surface tension. The soap also serves to make the vortex visible.

Properties of Liquids – Experiment # 7:
THE INCREDIBLE FLOATING YEN

Objective: To examine the effects of surface tension in water.

Materials:
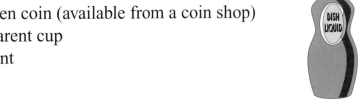
- Japanese 1 yen coin (available from a coin shop)
- Clear transparent cup
- Dish detergent
- Paper clip

Safety Precautions: None

Procedure:
1. Partially unbend the paper clip so it forms a 90° angle.
2. Rest the yen on the paper clip and carefully lower it onto the surface of a cup filled with water.
3. Gently lower and remove the paper clip. The yen should float. Observe at eye level.
4. Add a drop of liquid dish detergent. What happens?

Explanation: Water molecules exhibit surface tension because they are strongly attracted to one another. This is due to the polar nature of water molecules. Even though the yen is made from aluminum, which is denser than water, it still floats because the surface tension of water holds it up. Water has a density of 1 g/cc and aluminum has a density of 2.7 g/cc.

When the dish detergent is added, the surface tension of the water is destroyed, causing the yen to sink. The detergent molecules come in between the water molecules, breaking up the surface tension.

Properties of Liquids – Experiment # 8:
A HOMEMADE WATER THERMOMETER

Objective: To discover how a thermometer works.

Materials:

- Stove
- Electric drill
- Glass bottle
- Drinking straw
- Pan or beaker
- Food coloring

Safety Precautions: Perform only under adult supervision. Exercise caution with hot water. Handle bottle with potholders.

Procedure:

1. Drill a hole in the top of the jar lid so that a drinking straw will fit snugly through it.
2. Fill the bottle with water to the brim. Add a few drops of food coloring.
3. Place the lid on the jar. Insert the drinking straw through the hole in the jar lid so that it touches the bottom of the jar.
4. Place the jar inside a pan half-filled with water. Heat the water on the stove.
5. Observe the water in the straw as the water is heated.

Explanation: As water is heated its molecules move faster, causing them to spread farther apart from one another. As a result heated water expands, causing the water to rise in the straw. Thermometers work according to the same principle. As the liquid (usually mercury or alcohol) is heated, it expands and rises. As it cools, it contracts and falls.

CHAPTER 6
PROPERTIES
OF SOLIDS

Solids represent the third state of matter we will discuss. A solid has a definite shape and a definite volume. They cannot readily be compressed. Solids tend to be more dense than liquids or gases, although there are exceptions. All metals are solid at room temperature, except for mercury. Solids tend to have fairly strong bonds between their atoms, which make them rigid.

In this short chapter, we will examine the effect of heating on solids . . .

Properties of Solids – Experiment # 1:
DO METALS EXPAND WHEN HEATED?

Objective: To determine the effect of heating on the expansion rate of different metals.

Materials:
- Propane torch
- Metal tongs
- Two-dollar Canadian coin

Safety Precautions: Do only under adult supervision. Exercise caution when using propane torch. Do not touch coin when it is hot.

Procedure:
1. Heat the coin strongly over a propane torch for several minutes, and then plunge it into a cup of water.
2. Repeat the above step several times, until the little coin in the center falls out!

Explanation: The two-dollar Canadian coin is composed of two different types of metals – the outer ring is composed primarily of nickel and the inner portion is brass. The outer nickel ring is what makes the coin magnetic. When the coin is heated, both metals expand, but at different rates. The nickel expands a little more than does the brass; therefore the brass center falls out after continued heating.

This same phenomenon is at work in a typical thermostat in your home, which makes use of a bimetallic strip composed of two different metals. Since these two metals expand at different rates when heated, the strip curls, which triggers the thermostat. A dial thermometer also uses a bimetallic strip, as well as irons, toasters, and portable electric space heaters. Even the blinking lights on a Christmas tree utilize a bimetallic strip. When heated, the strip bends on the blinker light, shutting off the current and causing the lights to go out. When cooled, the strip bends back, causing current to flow again and the lights to come back on. This blinking on and off continues indefinitely as this tiny bimetallic strip becomes heated and then cools. That is why it usually takes a few minutes for the lights to start blinking after they are plugged in.

Bridges made of metal always have spaces between individual sections to prevent buckling in hot weather. Running jar lids under hot water makes them easier to open. This is due to the fact that metals expand as they are heated.

Properties of Solids – Experiment # 2:
SHATTERING A MARBLE

Objective: To discover the effect of heating and rapidly cooling a marble.

Materials: • Glass marbles
                   • Stove
                   • Cup of water
                   • Tongs
                   • Frying pan

Safety Precautions: Perform only under adult supervision. Wear safety goggles. Exercise caution when using stove. The marble will be very hot for several minutes after it is placed in water.

Procedure: 1. Place a marble in a frying pan and heat for about 10 minutes on the stove.
2. Using tongs, remove the marble from the pan and drop it in a cup of cold water.
3. Allow to cool for several minutes, then remove the marble. Observe.

Explanation: As the marble is heated, it expands. When it is cooled, it contracts. If it contracts too rapidly, it will shatter. This is why it is not a good idea to put water in a hot piece of glassware. Since the marble is spherical, it contracts equally in all directions, shattering the inside of the marble while still retaining its spherical shape.

CHAPTER 7
SOLUTIONS
AND
SOLUBILITY

A solution is also known as a homogeneous mixture, meaning it has a uniform composition throughout. It is composed of a solute dissolved within a solvent. In a true solution, the solute molecules will never settle out. Salt water, Kool-Aid, and soda pop are all examples of true solutions.

Solubility refers to the ability of a solute to dissolve in a solvent. When something dissolves, the particles become so small that they are rendered invisible. It is for this reason that solutions are always transparent, allowing light to pass through. A substance that does not dissolve in another is termed insoluble.

As the experiments on the following pages will demonstrate, solutions are all around us and solubility affects many aspects of our lives . . .

Solutions and Solubility – Experiment # 1:
WHY WATER AND OIL DO NOT MIX

Objective: To discover why polar and nonpolar substances
do not dissolve in one another.

Materials:
- Magnetic marbles (available from a toy or hobby store)
- Marbles
- Plastic cup

Safety Precautions: None

Procedure: 1. Add about a dozen or so magnetic marbles to the same number of ordinary marbles in a plastic cup.
2. Shake the marbles vigorously. Remove the marbles and observe.

Explanation: This simple little experiment very clearly shows why certain substances, like water and oil, do not mix. It is easy to see why the magnetic marbles all tend to stick together. Each magnet has two poles, and the pole of one magnet is attracted to the opposite pole of another. The ordinary marbles are not at all attracted to the magnetic marbles. Therefore the ordinary marbles are effectively separated from the magnetic marbles.

Molecules can also have poles, just like magnets. These molecules are termed polar, and have a distinct positively and negatively charged end. Water is an example of a polar molecule. A nonpolar molecule does not have distinct positive and negative ends, but is neutral throughout. Oil is an example of a nonpolar molecule.

The reason oil and water do not mix is because the water molecules are polar, and thus have a strong attraction for one another, just like the magnetic marbles. The oil molecules, being nonpolar, are not attracted to the water molecules, and are forced to aggregate together. They then float to the top because they are less dense than water molecules.

Solutions and Solubility – Experiment # 2:
THE MYSTERIOUS DISAPPEARING FLUID

Objective: To discover the effects of hydrogen bonding on the formation of a solution.

Materials:

- Long plastic tube from 30 – 90 cm. long (available from an aquarium dealer)
- Two corks or stoppers to fit the tube
- Food coloring
- 91% Isopropyl alcohol (or any other alcohol – the more concentrated the better)

Safety Precautions: Do only under adult supervision. Alcohol is poisonous and flammable. Keep away from open flames.

Procedure:
1. Place the stopper in one end of the tube and fill halfway with alcohol.
2. On top of the alcohol, add colored water until the tube is filled completely to the top. Replace the stopper. Some fluid will overflow, which is all right.
3. Invert the tube back and forth several times, until a large "bubble" appears. Note the level of fluid in the tube.

Explanation: The level of fluid in the tube will fall considerably, even though no fluid has leaked out! Alcohol and water mixed take up less space than they do while separate. Since alcohol molecules are quite a bit larger than water molecules, as they bond together their overall volume decreases. For a simple analogy, pour a half cup of water into a half cup of marbles. The end result will not be a full cup, since the water fills in the spaces between the marbles. In the same way, the water fills in the spaces that exist between the larger alcohol molecules.

The specific type of bonding that occurs in this experiment is known as hydrogen bonding. Hydrogen bonding occurs when the hydrogen atom of a water molecule bonds with an adjoining molecule of the opposite charge. A hydrogen atom within a water molecule will have a slightly positive charge, so it will be attracted to that portion of the alcohol molecule that has a slightly negative charge. Both alcohol and water are polar, so they are readily attracted to one another.

Hydrogen bonding does not lead to the formation of a compound, but rather is an example of intermolecular bonding. An intermolecular bond is a weak attraction that holds two adjacent molecules together. Hydrogen bonding occurs between adjacent water molecules, as well as between water and alcohol.

The tube should also feel warm, because any time a bond is formed energy is released. The formation of hydrogen bonds between the water and the alcohol release energy.

Solutions and Solubility – Experiment # 3:
A ROOT BEER FOUNTAIN

Objective: To discover how the solubility of a gas in a liquid is affected by temperature.

Materials:
- Propane torch
- Aluminum cylinder or large metal bolt that will fit into a 2-L bottle
- 2-L bottle of root beer
- Basin or dish pan to collect overflow
- Metal tongs

Safety Precautions: Perform only under adult supervision. Exercise caution when using propane torch.

Procedure:
1. Using tongs, heat the piece of metal over the propane torch for several minutes.
2. Drop the piece of metal into the bottle of root beer.
3. Stand back as you watch a spectacular root beer fountain, usually shooting several feet into the air!

Explanation: As the piece of hot metal is dropped into the bottle of root beer, the root beer heats up considerably, causing many CO_2 molecules to come out of solution. As a result, there is a massive eruption of root beer from the bottle. This shows that less gas can be dissolved in a warmer solution than in a colder one. As the temperature of a fluid increases, the kinetic energy of the gas molecules within that fluid also increases. This causes them to diffuse out of the fluid much more quickly. You may have noticed while pouring soda that warm soda tends to fizz more than cold soda. CO_2 diffuses more quickly out of warmer solutions than colder ones due to the decreased solubility of gases in warmer solutions.

This experiment also helps us understand the concept of thermal pollution. Thermal pollution occurs when factories dump massive amounts of otherwise clean but very hot water into streams and lakes. This causes dissolved oxygen to diffuse out of the water, which leads to the death of fish and other aquatic life.

This demonstration also illustrates the concept of nucleation sites. The hot piece of metal acts as a gigantic nucleation site, providing a place for many CO_2 molecules to adhere and aggregate, thus forcing them out of solution.

Solutions and Solubility – Experiment # 4:
SOLUTION OR SUSPENSION?

Objective: To differentiate between solutions and suspensions

Materials:

- Overhead projector
- Transparent plastic cups
- Unopened can of a clear carbonated beverage
- Other samples of soda
- Milk
- Muddy water

Safety Precautions: None

Procedure:

1. Place a transparent cup on the overhead projector.
2. Quickly open the can of clear soda and pour it into the cup. The projected image will initially turn black, then eventually turn clear!
3. Illuminate cups of cola, milk, and muddy water on the overhead. Observe.

Explanation: This demonstration graphically illustrates the difference between a solution and a suspension. A solution is a homogeneous mixture with only one phase. It will never settle out, and will always be transparent. A suspension is heterogeneous, having two or more distinct phases. Muddy water is a temporary suspension, where the dispersed particles will eventually settle to the bottom. Substances like milk are also suspensions, since particles are dispersed rather than dissolved.

   On the overhead, solutions will appear transparent, since the dissolved particles are so small that light can easily pass through the solution. Colas, coffee, and Kool-Aid will appear transparent on the overhead, proving that light can pass through them and that they are true solutions. Substances like milk and muddy water contain much larger particles, which do not allow light to pass. These substances are suspensions, not solutions.

   When the can of clear soda is poured into the cup on the overhead, the projected image will at first appear black, because of bubbles coming out of solution. At this point, the soda is not a solution, since there are two separate phases – a liquid and a gas. As soon as the bubbles dissipate, however, the soda appears clear. It is interesting to note that before the can is opened, the soda is a true solution, since the CO_2 is dissolved in the liquid. Upon opening, the bubbles begin to come out of solution, due to reduced pressure, forming a heterogeneous mixture.

Solutions and Solubility – Experiment # 5:
DOES THE FIZZ-KEEPER REALLY KEEP THE FIZZ?

Objective: To discover whether the Fizz-Keeper pump cap can keep a 2-L bottle of soda from going flat.

Materials:
- Two 2-L bottles of the same brand of soda
- Fizz-Keeper pump cap (available from the grocery store or a department store)

Safety Precautions: Wear safety goggles. To avoid overpressurizing the bottle, do not pump up the bottle with the Fizz-Keeper more than 100 times. When releasing the pressure, unscrew the Fizz-Keeper slowly from the bottle. Never aim the Fizz-Keeper at another person, and never place your face directly over the Fizz-Keeper, especially when unscrewing it from the bottle. Never use the Fizz-Keeper on a glass bottle.

Procedure:

1. Pour off liquid until the two bottles are about half full.
2. Replace the cap on one bottle, and pump up the other bottle with the Fizz-Keeper until it is firm. Do not pump more than 100 times.
3. Check the bottles in 24 hours. Test for firmness by squeezing both bottles, then pour some soda from each into cups to determine which contains the most fizz.

Explanation: The Fizz-Keeper is advertised as a device that prevents soda from going flat, by adding air to the bottle. Results will vary with this experiment, but often it appears that the Fizz-Keeper actually does little to prevent soda from going flat, at least over periods of 24 hours or longer. Also, a regular bottle cap seems to provide a better airtight seal than does the Fizz-Keeper.

Adding air to the space above the soda will do little to prevent carbon dioxide from diffusing out of the soda and filling the empty space above the soda in the bottle. If carbon dioxide was pumped into this space, it would have a much greater effect, since the rate of diffusion of carbon dioxide out of the soda is only affected by the pressure of carbon dioxide gas that exists in the space above the soda.

Henry's Law states that the solubility of a gas within a liquid is directly proportional to the pressure of that same gas on the liquid's surface. In other words, increasing the

pressure of carbon dioxide in the space above a bottle of soda will increase the rate at which carbon dioxide dissolves. Decreasing the pressure of CO_2 gas in the space above a bottle of solution will cause more CO_2 to diffuse out of the bottle, causing it to go flat. If you squeeze a brand new bottle of soda, the bottle will be very firm. There are over 4 atmospheres (atm) of CO_2 pressure in the space above the soda, serving to prevent excess CO_2 from escaping, thus keeping the soda fizzy. (Normal atmospheric pressure is 1 atm.)

Solutions and Solubility – Experiment # 6:
WHAT HAPPENS TO SODA WHEN IT IS BOILED?

Objective: To discover the effect of boiling on the properties of a carbonated beverage.

Materials:
- Hot plate
- Large pan
- 2-Liter bottle of soda
- Disposable cups
- Ice

Safety Precautions: Exercise caution when using the stove.

Procedure:
1. Pour a 2-Liter bottle of soda into a clean large pan.
2. Heat over a hot plate or stove until boiling.
3. Add ice to cool, and then serve in cups.
4. Note the taste.

Explanation: Soda that has been boiled will taste very flat. Less CO_2 can be dissolved in a heated solution because the gas molecules are moving so quickly that they diffuse out of the solution. By boiling soda, nearly all of the CO_2 will be forced out. The resulting solution will taste flat.

Solutions and Solubility – Experiment # 7:
MICROWAVEABLE SODA

Objective: To observe the effects of heating on a carbonated beverage.

Materials:

- Water-filled balloon
- Soda-filled balloon
- Microwave oven
- Funnel

Safety Precautions: Use a microwave only with adult supervision.

Procedure:

1. Blow up a balloon several times to stretch it out.
2. Fill it with water using a funnel.
3. Tie the balloon off, and place it in the center of a microwave oven.
4. Set the microwave for 10 minutes, and turn it on high. Record the time it takes for the water-filled balloon to burst.
5. Now place a soda-filled balloon in the center of the microwave oven. Make sure it contains the same amount of fluid as the water-filled balloon.
6. Set the microwave on high for ten minutes. Record the time it takes for this balloon to burst.
7. Compare the two times.

Explanation: As the microwaves heat the water in the balloon, it will expand to a tremendous size and then burst. As the water boils, the balloon expands to the breaking point as it fills with steam. The soda-filled balloon will also expand and burst, but in a much shorter time than the water-filled balloon. Because heating forces the CO_2 out of solution, the balloon will fill with CO_2 gas and burst. It is not even necessary for the soda to boil, since the expansion of the balloon is due solely to the escaping CO_2 gas. This demonstrates that gases are much less soluble in hot liquids than in cold.

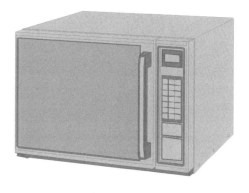

Solutions and Solubility – Experiment # 8:
WHAT COLOR IS IODINE?

Objective: To demonstrate that iodine is more soluble in oil than in alcohol.

Materials:
- Tincture of iodine (available from drugstore)
- Baby oil
- 20 oz. transparent soda bottle (or equivalent)

Safety Precautions: Perform only under adult supervision. Iodine is poisonous.

Procedure:
1. Squirt a little tincture of iodine into a bottle half-filled with water. It should be a uniform orange-brown color.
2. Add some baby oil until there is about a one centimeter layer floating on top.
3. Replace the cap and shake vigorously for one minute. Observe.

Explanation: This amazing experiment vividly demonstrates the nonpolar nature of iodine. Iodine is slightly soluble in water, but much more soluble in alcohol. Tincture of iodine is primarily a mixture of iodine and alcohol. But iodine is much more soluble in oil than in alcohol. Therefore, when oil is added to the tincture of iodine, the iodine readily dissolves in the oil. The violet color of the oil layer is characteristic of the true color of iodine.

The basic principle demonstrated here is that like dissolves like. This means that polar substances tend to dissolve in other polar substances, and nonpolar substances tend to dissolve in other nonpolar substances. A polar substance contains both a positive and a negative end, like the poles of the Earth or the poles of a magnet. Substances like water, alcohol, and acetone are all polar to varying degrees, and readily dissolve in one another. A nonpolar substance does not contain distinct positive and negative poles, but tends toward being neutral. Oils and fats are nonpolar. A nonpolar substance will not dissolve in a polar substance. This is why oil and water do not mix. But one nonpolar substance will tend to dissolve in another nonpolar substance. This is why iodine readily dissolves in baby oil. The baby oil has a much greater affinity (attraction) for the iodine than does the alcohol.

Solutions and Solubility – Experiment # 9:
A NOVEL WAY TO CLEAN UP AN OIL SPILL

Objective: To discover the amazing oil absorbing properties of hair.

Materials:

- Pair of women's nylon tights
- Kitchen-sized trash bag full of human hair (available in large quantities from any barber shop)
- Quart of motor oil
- One or two gallon transparent aquarium tank

Safety Precautions: Perform only under adult supervision. Motor oil is poisonous. This experiment is very messy – do outdoors if possible.

Procedure:

1. Cut one leg from the nylon tights and stuff the foot and part of the leg with hair and then tie the end into a knot.
2. Fill the aquarium about halfway with water and pour in about a half-quart of oil.
3. Submerge the hair-filled stocking into the oil and allow it to sit for a few minutes.
4. Remove the stocking. Most of the oil should be gone!
5. Remove any residual oil by sprinkling some loose hair on the surface of the water.

Explanation: Hair is seldom used for cleaning up oil spills, even though it is highly effective at doing so. We all know that hair gets oily if not washed, yet the extent to which hair can absorb oil is truly remarkable. Since oil and hair are both nonpolar, oil tends to be attracted to hair. This enables the hair to effectively soak up large quantities of oil. The outer layer of hair is composed of cuticles that overlap, similar to the scales on a fish. This outer cuticle layer has a very strong affinity for oil molecules. This layer also greatly increases the surface area of each strand of hair, which greatly increases its absorbing ability.

It has been calculated that 1.4 pounds of human hair could have theoretically absorbed all 11 million gallons of oil from the infamous Exxon Valdez oil spill in Alaska in 1989. Instead, two billion dollars were spent on a very lengthy cleanup that only captured about 12% of the oil.

Solutions and Solubility – Experiment # 10:
MAGIC SAND

Objective: To examine the properties of hydrophobic sand.

Materials:
- Hydrophobic sand (Available in toy and craft stores under various names, such as Magic Sand, Mystic Sand, or Squand. Or purchase in bulk from the Clifford Estes Co. at 973-890-2220.)
- Transparent plastic cups
- Vegetable oil

Safety Precautions: None

Procedure:
1. Add some magic sand to a cup of water. Pour off the water. Observe the appearance of the sand.
2. Pour a little magic sand into a small amount of vegetable oil in a cup. Pour off the oil. Observe the appearance of the sand.

Explanation: The magic sand is an amazing substance that will not get wet in water. It forms spectacular formations underwater, and when the water is poured off, it is completely dry. One advertising slogan for this substance is "You can bet it won't get wet!" Magic sand is made from ordinary sand, which is colored. It is then coated with a hydrophobic substance similar to wax that repels water. Hydrophobic literally means "fear of water." The substance used to coat the sand is nonpolar, which is why it repels water.

When added to oil, however, the sand does get wet. This is because the nonpolar coating over the wax is attracted to oil, another nonpolar substance. Since like dissolves like, a nonpolar substance will generally dissolve in another nonpolar substance. The magic sand was once thought to have real potential in cleaning up oil spills, but the fact that it is denser than water is a serious drawback.

Solutions and Solubility – Experiment # 11:
THE MYSTERIOUS MOVING CHADS

Objective: To demonstrate that nonpolar substances are attracted to other nonpolar substances.

Materials:
- Pencil
- 3 x 5 inch index card
- Mineral oil
- 20 oz. plastic soda bottle
- Transparent plastic cup

Safety Precautions: Perform only under adult supervision. Mineral oil is poisonous.

Procedure: 1. Using a pencil, very darkly color one entire side of a 3 x 5 card.
2. Using a hole punch, obtain about 20 – 30 chads from the card you just colored. These will be colored with a pencil on one side and blank on the other.
3. Add a little water to the bottle. Add about a half-centimeter layer of mineral oil.
4. Add the chads to the bottle, replace the cap, and shake.
5. Pour the contents into a plastic cup. Observe the orientation of the chads.

Explanation: This amazing little experiment always yields excellent results. When the contents of the bottle are poured into the cup, the chads will be floating on the interface between the water and the oil. But they will all be oriented in the same direction, with the dark side up and the white side down!

A pencil "lead" is not really made of lead, but graphite, which is a form of carbon. As are all pure elements, graphite is nonpolar in nature. Mineral oil is also nonpolar. Therefore the nonpolar graphite side of the chads will always be attracted to the nonpolar mineral oil. This is further verification of the principle that "like dissolves like."

Solutions and Solubility – Experiment # 12:
HOW TO MAKE CLEAR ICE

Objective: To discover why ice cubes are sometimes clear and sometimes cloudy.

Materials: • Two transparent plastic cups
                 • Freezer
                 • Hot and cold water

Safety Precautions: Exercise caution when boiling water.

Procedure: 1. Place cold tap water in one cup. In the second cup place water that has boiled for several minutes.
2. Place both in the freezer overnight.
3. Remove both cups and observe the appearance of each.

Explanation: The ice made with hot water should be very clear, while the ice made with cold water should be cloudy. This cloudiness is due to the presence of dissolved air in the cold water, which comes out of solution as the water freezes. Since water freezes fastest on the surface, the air that comes out of solution is driven inward toward the middle of the ice.

The ice made with hot water should be relatively clear, since hot water contains very little dissolved air. If you draw a glass of hot water from the tap, it will be cloudy for a few seconds and then will become clear. The cloudiness is due to air coming out of solution. This demonstrates that gases are much less soluble in hot liquids than in cold. As liquids are heated, the gases that are dissolved within are also heated. This causes them to gain kinetic energy, which makes them move faster and diffuse out of solution very quickly.

Solutions and Solubility – Experiment # 13:
DO YOUR HANDS GET WRINKLY IN THE OCEAN?

Objective: To discover what causes your hands to get wrinkly in water.

Materials: • Two large plastic cups
                  • Salt

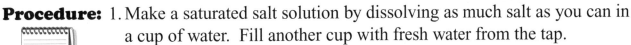

Safety Precautions: None

Procedure: 1. Make a saturated salt solution by dissolving as much salt as you can in a cup of water. Fill another cup with fresh water from the tap.
2. Submerge one hand in the salt water and the other in the fresh water for 20 minutes. Observe both hands.

Explanation: You should notice that your hand gets wrinkly from soaking in fresh water, just like being in the bathtub. However, the hand that was soaking in salt water will not be wrinkly at all! Every cell in the skin of your hands contains a semipermeable membrane, which allows some substances to enter the cell, but not others. Water can freely pass in and out of the cells of your skin. Whether water passes in or out depends on the concentration of salt outside of the cells. If your cells are surrounded by a solution that has a greater concentration of salt, water will pass from these cells to the outside solution in an attempt to equalize the concentrations. This passage of water through a semipermeable membrane is known as osmosis. If the concentration of salt is greater within the cells than outside, water will move into the cells. Water will always move in the direction of the greatest salt concentration, in an attempt to dilute it.

When placing your hand in tap water the solute concentration in the cells of your skin is greater than that of the tap water. The cells have a greater concentration of dissolved solutes than the water surrounding them. The cells are hypertonic to the surrounding solution. As a result, water will flow into the cells in an attempt to equalize the concentrations. This makes the skin wrinkly.

However, the solute concentration of the salt water is greater than that of the solute concentration in the cells. The cells have a lower concentration of dissolved solutes than the salt solution surrounding them. The cells are hypotonic to the surrounding solution. In an attempt to equalize the concentrations, water will actually leave the cells of your skin, making your skin feel a little tighter. This is how bath salts work, which prevent your skin from getting wrinkly as you soak in the tub. Remember to check your fingers the next time you swim in the ocean!

Solutions and Solubility – Experiment # 14:
FUN WITH POP ROCKS

Objective: To determine what influences the rate of popping of Pop Rocks candy.

Materials:
- Pop Rocks candy
- Transparent plastic cups
- Hot and cold water

Safety Precautions: None

Procedure: Obtain a cup of cold and hot water. Drop Pop Rocks into each. Observe the rate of popping. Save some to stick on your tongue!

Explanation: Pop Rocks candy produces a tingling, popping sensation when placed on the tongue. This candy is composed primarily of sugar, and is manufactured with carbon dioxide gas inside. When placed on the tongue, the sugar dissolves, releasing the carbon dioxide. This produces the strange fizzy feeling in your mouth.

Since sugar dissolves faster in hot water, the Pop Rocks will pop more quickly in hot water than in cold. In hot water the molecules are moving much faster, so there are more collisions with the sugar molecules, which increases the rate of dissolving. In cold water there are less collisions, so the rate of dissolving, and hence the rate of popping, is slower.

There is a new candy bar on the market called Xolander, which is manufactured by the Willy Wonka Candy Factory. Its slogan is "tongue crackling chocolate." It too is manufactured with carbon dioxide gas within the candy, which is released when eaten.

Solutions and Solubility – Experiment # 15:
MAKING A "FLOWMOTION" TUBE

Objective: To observe interesting flow patterns in a fluid.

Materials:
- Liquid hand soap containing glycol stearate, not glycol distearate (some, but not all, brands of Softsoap will work)
- 20 oz. plastic soda bottle, or other suitable container
- Food coloring

Safety Precautions: None

Procedure:
1. Fill about one-fourth of the bottle with liquid soap.
2. Add 5 drops of food coloring.
3. Slowly fill with water to avoid suds. Fill to the brim.
4. Screw cap on tightly and shake until well mixed.
5. Invert the bottle to observe an interesting swirling pattern.

Explanation: The interesting patterns that develop when your bottle is inverted are due to adding much more soap that can be dissolved in the water. As a result, the water flows past these undissolved soap particles, creating interesting flow patterns. The food coloring makes these patterns more visible.

This same effect is visible in commercially available "Flowmotion" tubes, which are made from similar materials. You can also observe the swirls in a bottle of V-8 Splash fruit drink. The color swirls are even mentioned on the label, where it is noted they are a natural phenomenon. The swirls are likely produced by fruit juices that are not fully dissolved in the drink. As a result, the remaining liquid flows past this undissolved liquid, creating the swirling effect.

Solutions and Solubility – Experiment # 16:
TESTING MARGARINE FOR FAT CONTENT

Objective: To determine if low fat and nonfat margarine really contain less fat.

Materials:
- Regular, reduced fat, and nonfat margarine
- Microwave oven
- Beakers or transparent microwaveable cups
- Tablespoon measure

Safety Precautions: Perform only under adult supervision. Do not touch beakers after margarine has melted – they will be very hot. Use potholders.

Procedure:
1. Place 4 tablespoons of regular margarine in a beaker.
2. Heat in microwave for 30 seconds, or until all margarine has melted.
3. Repeat with reduced fat and nonfat margarine.
4. Compare the level of oil that rises to the top in each. What conclusion can you make?

Explanation: Margarine is an example of an emulsion – which is a uniform mixture of a polar and a nonpolar substance. Margarine is a mixture of water, oil, and other substances. Normally these would not mix, were it not for the presence of an emulsifier. An emulsifier contains both a polar and a nonpolar end, and forms a bridge between polar and nonpolar substances so that they stay mixed. Lecithin is a common emulsifier used in margarine. It enables the oil to stay mixed in with the water and other substan-ces, giving the margarine a uniform composition.

When heated, lecithin breaks down, and the oil, usually soybean oil, rises to the top because it is less dense. There is a noticeable difference in the amount of oil between the three types of margarine. Regular margarine will have the most, reduced fat will have less, and nonfat will have none. It is also interesting to note that the volume of the margarine in each case decreases considerably. This is because air is whipped into the mixture during its manufacture, which contributes to its creamy texture. Upon heating, this air escapes. This is noticeable as foam on top of the mixture as it heats.

Would you expect similar results if this experiment was attempted with butter? Try it and find out.

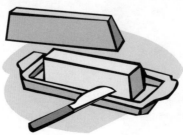

Solutions and Solubility – Experiment # 17:
DOES WATER CONDUCT ELECTRICITY?

Objective: To discover if water conducts electricity.

Materials:

- 6-V lantern battery
- 6-V flashlight bulb (from a flashlight that uses a 6-V battery)
- Three wires with alligator clips attached (available at Radio Shack)
- Plastic cups
- Distilled water
- Salt (sodium chloride)
- Two copper strips or small copper tubing (available from hardware store)
- Sheet metal shears
- Vinegar
- Household ammonia
- Sugar (sucrose)

Safety Precautions: Use sheet metal shears only with adult supervision – be careful not to cut yourself. Make sure bulb is capable of supporting a 6-V battery, otherwise it will burn out. Ammonia is very toxic – do not inhale fumes.

Procedure:
1. Cut two strips of copper, each about 2 inches long and a half-inch wide. (If using copper tubing, cut two pieces, each about 2 inches long. Flatten one end of each with a hammer so the alligator clips can be attached.)
2. Attach the end of one wire to a battery terminal, and the other end of the wire to a copper strip.
3. Attach the end of the second wire to the other battery terminal, and the other end of the wire to the upper metal rim of the light bulb.
4. Attach the end of the third wire to the base of the light bulb, and the other end of the wire to the other copper strip.
5. Touch together both copper strips. The bulb should light up.
6. Fill the cup about halfway with distilled water. Place both copper strips into the water, so they are about a half-inch apart. Make sure they are not touching. Observe the light bulb.
7. Slowly add salt to the cup. What happens to the light bulb?
8. Repeat with tap water, vinegar, ammonia, sugar water, and other substances found around the house. Record your observations.

Explanation: Contrary to popular belief, pure water does not conduct electricity. (Actually it conducts very slightly, but is only measurable with very sensitive instruments.) It is actually the dissolved ions in water that conduct the electricity. When sodium chloride (NaCl) is added to water, it breaks down into Na^+ ions and Cl^- ions. Since opposite charges attract, the Na^+ ions are attracted to the cathode (negative terminal) and the Cl^- ions are attracted to the anode (positive terminal). Since current electricity is nothing more than the movement of charged particles, the movement of these ions completes the circuit, thus lighting the bulb.

Solutions that conduct electricity are known as electrolytes. Salt water is an excellent electrolyte. A body of water such as a lake or swimming pool will never be completely pure, so these are excellent electrolytes, which is why it is so dangerous to swim during an electrical storm.

Tap water will conduct electricity, because it will contain some dissolved mineral ions. You may or may not be able to detect this, depending on the mineral concentration of the tap water and the sensitivity of your apparatus. Vinegar and ammonia should both conduct, since acids and bases are excellent electrolytes. Acids ionize to form H^+ ions in water, and bases ionize to form OH^- ions in water.

The sugar water, if made with distilled water, will not conduct electricity. Sugar is an example of a covalent compound, which does not break down into ions in water. Instead, sugar breaks down into neutral molecules. It is for this reason that covalent compounds are also referred to as molecular compounds.

Ionic compounds will generally conduct electricity in aqueous solution. They will not conduct in the solid form, however. It is necessary to have freely moving ions in order to conduct, and this only happens in solution. Ionic compounds are also referred to as salts. We can thus conclude that acids, bases, and salts are electrolytes in aqueous solution. Molecular compounds in solution will generally be nonelectrolytes.

Solutions and Solubility – Experiment # 18:
MAGIC CRYSTALS

Objective: To create a beautiful underwater crystal garden.

Materials:

- Sodium silicate solution (available in the hardware store as Water Glass – in the paint section)
- Copper(II) sulfate (available in the hardware store as a root killer)
- Epsom salts
- Baby food jar

Safety Precautions: Do only under adult supervision. Wear safety goggles. Sodium silicate, copper(II) sulfate, and Epsom salts are all poisonous if ingested. Wash hands thoroughly after this experiment. Sodium silicate is irritating to the skin – do not touch.

Procedure:
1. Fill a baby food jar with sodium silicate solution.
2. Add a few crystals of copper(II) sulfate and Epsom salts.
3. Replace the lid. Observe over the next several hours and again the following day.

Explanation: The crystals dropped into the sodium silicate solution should have expanded to form beautiful stalagmite-like structures, with many narrow appendages extending from each crystal. The commercially available Magic Rocks also uses sodium silicate solution and several different types of crystals.

The key to the success of this experiment is the fact that the substances added to the solution are hydrates, which means that water molecules are part of their chemical composition. The formula for copper(II) sulfate is $CuSO_4 \bullet 5H_2O$. This means there are 5 water molecules bonded to each formula unit of copper(II) sulfate. Epsom salts are magnesium sulfate. The formula is $MgSO_4 \bullet 7H_2O$. There are 7 water molecules bonded to each formula unit of magnesium sulfate. This water can be driven off by heating.

When the crystals are initially dropped into the sodium silicate solution, a double displacement reaction occurs. For copper(II) sulfate, the reaction is as follows:
$$CuSO_{4(aq)} + Na_2SiO_{3(aq)} \longrightarrow Na_2SO_{4(aq)} + CuSiO_{3(s)}$$
The $CuSiO_3$ that forms will be a solid, because it is insoluble in water. Anytime two liquids react, and one of the resulting products is a solid, a precipitate has most likely formed. In the above reaction, copper(II) silicate ($CuSiO_3$) forms a precipitate.

When the Epsom salts are added to the sodium silicate solution, the following reaction occurs: $MgSO_{4(aq)} + Na_2SiO_{3(aq)} \longrightarrow Na_2SO_{4(aq)} + MgSiO_{3(s)}$
In the above reaction, magnesium silicate ($MgSiO_3$) forms the precipitate.

The precipitates that form above still contain water molecules within their chemical structures. However, compared to the concentration of water in the surrounding solution, this is only a tiny bit of water. The precipitates act as a semipermeable membrane. This membrane allows some substances to pass through but not others. Water is one substance that can pass through. In an attempt to dilute the water solution inside the membrane, water will pass by osmosis into the crystals through this semipermeable membrane. Water always passes from a region of higher water concentration to one of lower water concentration. As water continues to pass into the crystals, they continue to grow, producing the beautiful stalagmite formations.

Stalagmites are natural mineral formations that grow from the ground up in caves. These natural stalagmites form by a different process than the ones created in this experiment.

If available, cobalt(II) chloride produces very beautiful crystals using the above process. Experiment with other solids to see what they do.

Solutions and Solubility – Experiment # 19:
MRS. STEWART'S LIQUID BLUING CRYSTAL GARDEN

Objective: To form a beautiful sodium chloride crystal "garden."

Materials:
- Aluminum pie pan
- Mrs. Stewart's Liquid Bluing (available in the laundry detergent section of the grocery store)
- Sponge, charcoal, or brick pieces
- Salt (sodium chloride)
- Household ammonia
- Food coloring (optional)

Safety Precautions: Do only under adult supervision. Wear safety goggles. Liquid bluing and household ammonia are both toxic if ingested. Wash hands thoroughly when finished. Do not inhale ammonia fumes.

Procedure:
1. Break up and place several pieces of charcoal, brick, or a household sponge in an aluminum pie pan.
2. Carefully spread 30 mL each of water, bluing, ammonia, and salt over the contents of the pan.
3. Pour another 30 mL of salt over the garden the next day.
4. The following day, add 30 mL of water, bluing, salt, and ammonia to the bottom of the pan. Do not pour directly on the base material. If desired, add a few drops of food coloring at this point.
5. Observe over the next few days and weeks.
6. Sparingly add more water, salt, and bluing every week or so to keep the garden growing.

Explanation: The sponge or other base material is very porous, greatly increasing the surface area and increasing the rate of evaporation of the water. As water evaporates, the sodium chloride is left behind. The liquid bluing particles form a nucleation site, or a place where the sodium chloride can adhere and get started. Once a single formula unit of sodium chloride adheres to a bluing particle, it attracts other formula units of sodium chloride. These always form in a cubic formation, which is characteristic of sodium chloride. Eventually the entire surface of the pan will be covered with a beautiful delicate coating of coral-like sodium chloride crystals. These will eventually climb out of the pan and continue to spread.

The purpose of adding the ammonia is to hasten the rate of evaporation when it mixes with the water, since ammonia evaporates more quickly than water.

150 More Captivating Chemistry Experiments Using Household Substances

Solutions and Solubility – Experiment # 20:
REUSABLE COLD PACK

Objective: To understand the concept of freezing point depression by making a reusable cold pack.

Materials:
- Quart freezer bag
- Isopropyl rubbing alcohol
- Food coloring (optional)

Safety Precautions: Isopropyl alcohol is poisonous if ingested. Be sure to clearly label the bag "POISON" before putting it into the freezer.

Procedure: 1. Add 2 cups of water and 1 cup of alcohol to a freezer bag and seal.
2. Place in the freezer overnight.
3. Observe the bag.

Explanation: The solution in the bag will not freeze, because alcohol has a much lower freezing point than water. Isopropyl alcohol freezes at -89° C, and water freezes at 0°C. As a result, alcohol will depress the freezing point of the water. The temperatures in a typical freezer are not cold enough to freeze the solution.

The cold pack that was made in this experiment can be used whenever cold is required for an injury, such as to reduce swelling. It can then be placed in the freezer and used over and over again.

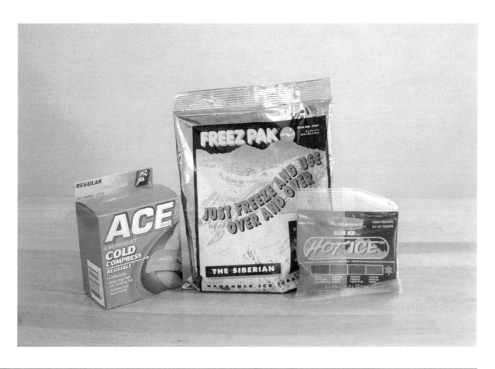

Solutions and Solubility – Experiment # 21:
TESTING FOR HARD WATER

Objective: To determine the effect of hard water on the production of soap suds.

Materials:
- Three 20 oz. plastic soda bottles
- Epsom salts (magnesium sulfate – $MgSO_4$)
- Distilled water
- Liquid dishwashing detergent

Safety Precautions: Epsom salts are toxic if ingested.

Procedure:
1. Add 100 mL of tap water to the 1st bottle, 100 mL of distilled water to the 2nd bottle, and 100 mL of tap water + a teaspoon of Epsom salts to the third bottle.
2. Add 1 drop of liquid dishwashing detergent to each bottle and shake each vigorously.
3. Measure the height of the column of soap suds in each bottle.

Explanation: Hard water is water that contains an excess of magnesium or calcium ions. This water is termed "hard" because it is hard to get such water to form suds when soap is added. These ions react with the soap to form what is commonly referred to as soap scum. This soap scum is a precipitate containing either magnesium or calcium ions. Only when all of these ions have precipitated can soap suds form. This results in one having to use a lot of soap, and an undesirable soap scum that can be difficult to remove.

Water containing a small amount of magnesium or calcium ions is referred to as soft water. Distilled water is obviously soft because it is pure water. Comparing the amount of suds in your tap water to the distilled water will give you an idea how hard your water is. If there is a noticeable difference, then your tap water is hard. City water is not likely to be hard, but well water often is. Adding the Epsom salts to the third bottle made the water very hard because a portion of the soap reacted with the Mg^{2+} ions instead of forming suds. This bottle probably produced the least amount of suds.

Solutions and Solubility – Experiment # 22:

SOFTENING HARD WATER

Objective: To discover the best method for softening hard water.

Materials:
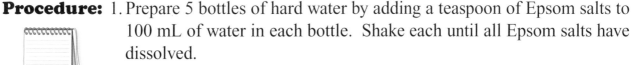
- Borax (sodium tetraborate)
- Washing soda (sodium carbonate)
- Household ammonia (nonsudsing)
- Calgon water softener (or other commercial water softener)
- Epsom salts (magnesium sulfate – $MgSO_4$)
- Eyedropper
- Liquid dishwashing detergent
- Five 20 oz. plastic soda bottles

Safety Precautions: Perform only under adult supervision. Borax and washing soda are poisonous if ingested, and extremely corrosive to eyes and skin.

Procedure:
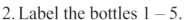
1. Prepare 5 bottles of hard water by adding a teaspoon of Epsom salts to 100 mL of water in each bottle. Shake each until all Epsom salts have dissolved.
2. Label the bottles 1 – 5.
3. Bottle 1 will be the control. No softener will be added.
4. To bottle 2, add a teaspoon of borax. Shake to dissolve.
5. To bottle 3, add a teaspoon of washing soda. Shake to dissolve.
6. To bottle 4, add a teaspoon of Calgon water softener. Shake to dissolve.
7. To bottle 5, add 20 drops of ammonia.
8. Add 1 drop of liquid dishwashing detergent to each of the above bottles.
9. Shake each bottle. Measure the column of soap suds produced in each. Which softener was the most effective?

Explanation: Each of the above substances should have been somewhat effective at softening the hard water. This is evident by the amount of suds produced. Softer water will produce more suds. Hard water can be softened by adding a substance that will react with the Mg^{2+} or Ca^{2+} ions and cause them to precipitate. Therefore the softener must be put in before the soap is added. If put in after the soap is added, the softener will have no effect, since the soap would already have reacted with the ions and would no longer be available to produce suds. Most laundry and dishwashing detergents already contain softeners, but the above methods can still be used if further softening is required.

The most common method of water softening used today is the ion exchange method. The hard water is passed through an active material containing sodium chloride. The sodium chloride exchanges its sodium ions for calcium and magnesium ions. The soft water will contain twice as many sodium ions as calcium and magnesium ions because the charge of the sodium ion is 1+, whereas the charge of each magnesium and calcium ions is 2+. But since sodium does not react with soap like calcium and magnesium does, the water is no considered longer hard.

CHAPTER 8
CHEMICAL REACTIONS

Chemical reactions represent the heart and soul of chemistry. The bonding together of two or more atoms to produce a compound with completely different properties than either of the constituent elements is one of the marvels of chemistry.

Consider common table salt, or sodium chloride. It is composed of sodium and chlorine. Sodium is a silvery metal that bursts into flames when added to water. Chlorine is a poisonous yellow-green gas that can be deadly if inhaled. Together, they form a white compound that we probably add to our food every day.

Water is composed of two gases – hydrogen and oxygen. Hydrogen is an explosive gas. Combustion could not occur without oxygen. Yet together, they combine to form water, which is used to put out fires.

The incredible world of chemical reactions awaits you on the following pages . . .

Chemical Reactions – Experiment # 1:
TESTING FOR COUNTERFEIT MONEY

Objective: To determine if U.S. paper currency is genuine or counterfeit.

Materials:
- Tincture of iodine (available from drug store)
- Counterfeit marking pen (available from office supply store)
- Dollar bill (or other currency)

Safety Precautions: Perform only under adult supervision. Iodine is very poisonous if ingested.

Procedure:
1. Using the counterfeit marking pen, place a mark on a dollar bill.
2. Now place a mark on a normal sheet of white paper using the counterfeit marking pen.
3. Now place a few drops of tincture of iodine on both the dollar bill and the sheet of white paper.

Explanation: The counterfeit marking pen will produce a yellow color on a dollar bill, but a deep blue-black color on a normal sheet of paper. The same color can be observed using the tincture of iodine. This clearly shows that the counterfeit marking pen uses an iodine solution to test for the presence of starch. All U.S. currency is made from special starch-free paper, which is not available to the general public. This starch-free paper will not react with iodine. Most types of paper, however, contain starch. Iodine reacts with starch to form the characteristic blue-black starch-iodine complex. The next time a store clerk marks your bill with one of these pens, make sure you explain to her the chemistry behind it!

150 More Captivating Chemistry Experiments Using Household Substances

Chemical Reactions – Experiment # 2:
BRIGHTLY GLOWING LIGHTSTICKS

Objective: To discover the effect of temperature on the rate of a reaction.

Materials:

- Lightstick (available from toy or sporting goods store)
- Scissors
- Test tube
- Test tube holders
- Propane torch

Safety Precautions: Perform only under adult supervision. Wear safety goggles. The liquid within a lightstick is toxic. Do not ingest or allow it to contact your skin.

Procedure:
1. Activate a lightstick by bending, which breaks a glass vial in the tube and causes a reaction to occur.
2. Carefully cut open the top of the lightstick with a sharp pair of scissors.
3. Pour the contents into a test tube and heat strongly over the flame of a propane torch. Observe.

Explanation: The lightstick contains (among other things) a substance known as luminol, which when mixed with an oxidizing agent in the glass vial, emits light. The emitted light does not give off heat, and is known as cold light. The production of light without heat due to a chemical reaction is known as chemiluminescence. The same reaction occurs in a firefly. When heated, the reaction occurs much more quickly, because reacting molecules are colliding more frequently. This causes the lightstick to glow brighter. If cooled, the lightstick would glow less brightly, because the rate of reaction would then be slowed. If immersed in liquid nitrogen, the lightstick will stop glowing completely!

Chemical Reactions – Experiment # 3:
TESTING FOR VITAMIN C

Objective: To discover if fruit drinks contain Vitamin C.

Materials:
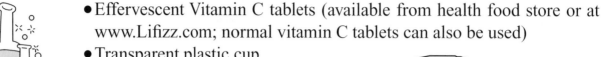
- Tincture of iodine (available from drug store)
- Effervescent Vitamin C tablets (available from health food store or at www.Lifizz.com; normal vitamin C tablets can also be used)
- Transparent plastic cup
- Spray starch (used for ironing)
- Variety of fruit drinks
- Eyedropper

Safety Precautions: Perform only under adult supervision. Iodine is poisonous if ingested. Vitamins can be toxic in large doses. Do not drink the results of any part of this experiment.

Procedure:
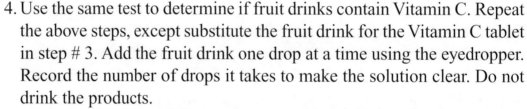
1. Place a few drops of tincture of iodine in a cup of water.
2. Spray some starch into the water. It should turn a deep blue color.
3. Drop in an effervescent vitamin C tablet. Observe. Do not drink.
4. Use the same test to determine if fruit drinks contain Vitamin C. Repeat the above steps, except substitute the fruit drink for the Vitamin C tablet in step # 3. Add the fruit drink one drop at a time using the eyedropper. Record the number of drops it takes to make the solution clear. Do not drink the products.
5. Compare the amount of vitamin C each drink has by recording the amounts of each it takes to clear up the starch-iodine solution. Again, do not drink the products, as iodine is poisonous.

Explanation: When starch is added to the iodine, the characteristic blue-black color of the starch-iodine complex appears. When the fizzy vitamin C tablet is added, the solution quickly turns clear. This is because vitamin C reduces the colored I_2 to the colorless I^-.

If a fruit drink containing vitamin C is added to the starch-iodine solution, it will turn colorless. A fruit drink that does not contain vitamin C will not have this effect. If a drink contains a large amount of Vitamin C, then less will be needed to cause the change from blue-black to colorless. If a drink contains only a small amount of vitamin C, more of the drink will be needed to cause this color change to occur.

Chemical Reactions – Experiment # 4:
HOW DOES DRANO WORK?

Objective: To discover how Drano is effective at unclogging drains.

Materials: • Drano drain cleaner – dry granular form. (If not available, lye and aluminum foil can be substituted.)
• Eyedropper
• Watch glass or sturdy glass plate
• pH paper or red cabbage juice (optional)

Safety Precautions: Drano is a very poisonous, highly caustic substance. It is primarily concentrated sodium hydroxide. Perform this experiment only under adult supervision. Wear safety goggles, as sodium hydroxide can cause permanent eye damage. Do not touch, as it will burn the skin. Read label thoroughly before using.

Procedure: 1. Place a small amount of Drano in the center of a watch glass. Add a few drops of water. Observe.

2. Repeat, except this time remove the small metal pieces. Now add water and observe.
3. Test the pH of the solution by using pH paper or red cabbage juice.

Explanation: Drano is composed of concentrated sodium hydroxide (lye) and tiny pieces of aluminum metal. In the dry form, they do not react, but when water is added, a very vigorous reaction takes place. The water causes the sodium hydroxide to dissolve, which breaks it into ions, greatly increasing the surface area of the substance. In aqueous solution, therefore, sodium hydroxide readily reacts with aluminum. This is easy to observe, since bubbles of gas are released from the tiny pieces of aluminum metal. The gas being given off is hydrogen. The reaction is as follows:

$$2NaOH_{(aq)} + 2Al_{(s)} + 2H_2O_{(l)} \longrightarrow 2NaAlO_{2(aq)} + 3H_{2(g)}$$

Aluminum is one of the few substances that will react with both an acid and a base. When the aluminum pieces are removed, no reaction takes place, because the addition of water to sodium hydroxide only results in the formation of a solution, not a new product. It is the hydrogen gas produced by the reaction of the sodium hydroxide with the aluminum that helps to unclog drains, because this release of gas can result in a buildup of pressure. Sodium hydroxide itself will also react with a wide variety of substances, since it is a strong base.

The fact that sodium hydroxide is basic can be proven by testing an aqueous solution of this substance with pH paper or red cabbage juice. Red cabbage juice is prepared by boiling some red cabbage leaves in water and then pouring out the juice, which will be a purplish color. It will turn green in a base and red in an acid.

Chemical Reactions – Experiment # 5:
HOW DOES SANI-FLUSH WORK?

Objective: To determine how Sani-Flush toilet bowl cleaner works.

Materials:

- Sani-Flush toilet bowl cleaner (dry granular form)
- Watch glass or sturdy glass plate
- Eyedropper
- pH paper or red cabbage juice (optional)
- Wooden coffee stirrer
- Matches

Safety Precautions: Perform this experiment only under adult supervision. Sani-Flush contains sodium bisulfate, which forms sulfuric acid in water. Wear safety goggles, as this substance can cause permanent eye damage. Do not touch, as it will burn the skin. Read label thoroughly before using. Exercise caution when using matches

Procedure:

1. Place a small amount of Sani-Flush crystals on a watch glass.
2. Add a few drops of water and observe.
3. Light the wooden coffee stirrer and place near the bubbling solution. What happens? Do not touch, as it will burn the skin.
4. Using pH paper or red cabbage juice, test the pH of the resulting solution.

Explanation: Sani-Flush is composed primarily of sodium bisulfate ($NaHSO_4$) and sodium bicarbonate or baking soda ($NaHCO_3$). When water is added, the sodium bisulfate reacts to form sulfuric acid. The equation is as follows:

$$NaHSO_{4(s)} \ + \ H_2O_{(l)} \longrightarrow H_2SO_{4(aq)} \ + \ Na^+_{(aq)}$$

The sulfuric acid then reacts with the sodium bicarbonate to produce carbon dioxide gas, which puts out the flame. The equation is as follows:

$$H_2SO_{4(aq)} \ + \ NaHCO_{3(s)} \longrightarrow Na_2SO_{4(aq)} \ + \ CO_{2(g)} \ + \ H_2O_{(l)}$$

Sani-Flush primarily works due to its strong acidic content, which can be verified by testing for its pH. It is the low pH of this substance that makes it effective at removing stains. Acids react with a wide variety of substances. The sodium bicarbonate actually has little effect, other than to produce bubbling and foaming when it reacts with the acid. This does little as far as stain removal goes, but does give the consumer the impression that it is working well since bubbles are being produced.

Chemical Reactions – Experiment # 6:
THE INCREDIBLE RISING MUSTARD

Objective: To discover what happens when baking soda is added to mustard.

Materials:
- Clear plastic cup
- Mustard
- Baking soda (sodium bicarbonate)

Safety Precautions: Wear safety goggles when performing this experiment.

Procedure: 1. Pour some mustard into the clear cup. The amount is not crucial.
2. Add a half-teaspoon of baking soda to the cup and stir briefly.
3. Cease stirring and observe.
4. Add baking soda a little at a time, until the reaction ceases.

Explanation: The mustard will rise in a dramatic fashion due to the presence of vinegar in mustard. The reaction between the vinegar and baking soda will produce carbon dioxide gas, which causes the mustard to rise. The reaction is as follows:

$$CH_3COOH_{(aq)} \quad + \quad NaHCO_{3(aq)} \longrightarrow \quad NaCH_3COO_{(aq)} \quad + \quad H_2O_{(l)} \quad + \quad CO_{2(g)}$$
$$\text{vinegar} \qquad\qquad \text{baking soda} \qquad\qquad\qquad \text{sodium acetate}$$

The reaction will continue until all of the vinegar (dilute acetic acid) is used up. In this case, the baking soda will be in excess. Since the vinegar is used up, it is the limiting reactant.

Try this experiment with other condiments such as ketchup, relish, and mayonnaise. What happens? Read the ingredients on the label to find out why.

Chemical Reactions – Experiment # 7:
WHY RIPE BANANAS TASTE SWEET

Objective: To discover the chemical difference between green and ripe bananas.

Materials:

- One green banana
- One overripe banana
- Kitchen knife
- Tincture of iodine (available from the drugstore)

Safety Precautions: Perform this experiment only under adult supervision. Iodine is poisonous if ingested. Do not eat the bananas after adding iodine.

Procedure:
1. Cut open the green banana and slice off a piece. Add a few drops of tincture of iodine. Observe.
2. Cut open the overripe banana and slice off a piece. Add a few drops of tincture of iodine. Observe.
3. Repeat with other samples of unripe and ripe fruits. What do you observe?

Explanation: The iodine turns a deep blue-black color in the presence of starch, due to the formation of the starch-iodine complex. Unripe bananas contain a great deal of starch, as evidenced by the color change when the iodine is added. However, as bananas ripen, this starch is converted to sugar. When iodine is added to a very ripe banana, there will be no color change, since sugar does not react with iodine.

Chemical Reactions – Experiment # 8:
THERMAL DECOMPOSITION OF BAKING SODA

Objective: To discover what happens when baking soda is heated.

Materials:

- Baking soda (sodium bicarbonate – $NaHCO_3$)
- Propane torch
- Test tube
- Test tube tongs
- Wood splint

Safety Precautions: Perform only under adult supervision. Exercise caution with propane torch. Wear safety goggles.

Procedure:
1. Place a spoonful of baking soda in a test tube.
2. Heat over the propane torch for several minutes.
3. While heating over the torch, insert a flaming wood splint into the mouth of the test tube. Observe.
4. Observe what collects on the walls of the test tube.

Explanation: When heated, sodium bicarbonate breaks down into sodium carbonate, water, and carbon dioxide. This is known as thermal decomposition.
The balanced chemical equation is as follows:

$$2NaHCO_{3(s)} \longrightarrow Na_2CO_{3(s)} + H_2O_{(g)} + CO_{2(g)}$$

Water can be readily observed collecting on the walls of the test tube. These water droplets have condensed from the steam being given off. The carbon dioxide can be detected by the fact that the flaming wood splint is extinguished. This demonstrates the value of baking soda as a fire extinguisher. When sprinkled on a fire, baking soda decomposes to give off carbon dioxide gas, which tends to displace oxygen because it is denser than air.

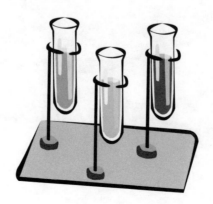

Chemical Reactions – Experiment # 9:
PREVENTING GREEN EGG YOLKS

Objective: To discover why hard-boiled egg yolks are sometimes green, and how to prevent this discoloration from occurring.

Materials:

- Two eggs
- Pan
- Stove
- Ice
- Tongs

Safety Precautions: Perform only under adult supervision. Exercise caution with boiling water.

Procedure:

1. Place two eggs in a pan of boiling water.
2. After ten minutes turn off the heat. Remove one egg with a pair of tongs and gently place in a bowl of water with ice cubes added.
3. Leave the other egg in the pan of hot water.
4. After 30 minutes, carefully peel both eggs and remove the yolks. Observe the color of each.

Explanation: The egg placed in the cold water should have a nice yellow color to the yolk, but the egg left in the hot water will have an unsightly green yolk. The green yolk is not harmful, but is unappetizing. There is much interesting chemistry at work here.

When an egg is cooked, hydrogen sulfide (H_2S) gas is released from the egg white. When eggs go bad, an excess of H_2S gas forms, which causes the rotten egg smell. But even fresh eggs will release some hydrogen sulfide gas upon cooking. This gas forms when the protein in the egg white is heated. Heating liberates some sulfur atoms from the protein, which combine with hydrogen ions in the egg white to yield hydrogen sulfide gas.

The green yolk is formed when H_2S gas migrates from the egg white to the egg yolk. The egg yolk contains iron, and the green color results from the reaction of hydrogen sulfide with iron. This produces iron(II) sulfide (FeS), which has a green color. The reaction is as follows:

$$H_2S_{(g)} + Fe_{(s)} \longrightarrow FeS_{(s)} + H_{2(g)}$$

Gases are much more soluble in cold solutions than in hot ones. Therefore as the egg is heated, the gas will migrate toward the center where it is cooler. The key to preventing green yolks is to get the hydrogen sulfide gas to move back out of the yolk. If the egg is allowed to remain in hot water, the H_2S gas remains in the center, where it reacts with the iron to form the green iron(II) sulfide. But if the egg is placed in cold water after cooking, then the outside of the egg is now colder than the inside. As a result, the gas will migrate out of the yolk and into the egg white. This is due to the fact that gases are much more soluble in colder solutions. So the H_2S will tend to move out of the yolk, since it is more soluble in the cooler egg white. As a result, the yolk will be an attractive yellow color.

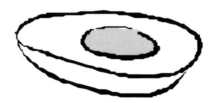

Chemical Reactions – Experiment # 10:
PAINTING WITH BLEACH

Objective: To observe the decolorizing effects of bleach.

Materials:

- Household bleach
- Inexpensive watercolor paintbrush
- Black construction paper

Safety Precautions: Perform this experiment only under adult supervision. Wear safety goggles. Bleach is extremely toxic if ingested, and is corrosive to the eyes and skin. Be careful not to spill on your clothing.

Procedure: 1. Dip the paintbrush in bleach and paint on the black paper. What happens?
2. Try painting on other colors of paper with bleach. What happens?

Explanation: Household bleach is a 5% solution of sodium hypochlorite (NaClO) in water. The hypochlorite ion (ClO⁻) is a strong oxidizer. An oxidizer causes another substance to be oxidized, or lose electrons. The hypochlorite ion oxidizes the compounds in colored dyes to colorless compounds. That is why bleach is so effective at removing stains. In this experiment, the dyes used to make colored paper are changed into colorless compounds by the oxidizing action of bleach. Bleaching is a good example of a chemical change, since the chemical composition of compounds is altered.

Chemical Reactions – Experiment # 11:
WHY SODA DOES NOT REACT WITH AN ALUMINUM CAN

Objective: To reveal the plastic liner inside of a pop can.

Materials:
- Steel wool (a coarser grade works best)
- Unopened can of soda
- Stirring rod or any long thin rod
- Copper(II) sulfate (available in hardware stores as a root killer)
- 1-L beaker or other container
- Table salt

Safety Precautions: Wear safety goggles and rubber gloves. Do this experiment only under adult supervision. Copper(II) sulfate is extremely poisonous if ingested. Do not touch this substance or the by-products. Wash hands thoroughly when finished. Place copper in a separate container when finished and take to a hazardous waste facility.

Procedure:
1. Using steel wool, completely remove the paint from a full, unopened can of soda. (This will take about 20 minutes.)
2. Pour out the soda, rinse, and fill the can with water.
3. Add 600 mL of water to the beaker. To this, add 8 teaspoons of copper(II) sulfate and 4 teaspoons of salt. Stir thoroughly until dissolved.
4. Insert a stirring rod through the pull tab on the top of the full can of water and lower into the solution in the beaker.
5. Adjust the can until it is level. Make sure the level of the solution is just below the top rim of the can.
6. Remove in about an hour. Observe.
7. Rinse off and display the result in a clean beaker.

Explanation: This is a fascinating experiment that is well worth the time it takes to prepare. A chemical reaction occurs between the aluminum can and the solution, completely removing the aluminum and revealing the liner, which is an extremely thin layer of plastic that completely coats the inside of the can. The liner prevents the acidic soda from reacting with the aluminum. The soda will not react with plastic.

Copper sulfate will react with aluminum in the presence of sodium chloride, which acts as a catalyst. The reaction is as follows:

$$3CuSO_{4(aq)} + 2Al_{(s)} \longrightarrow Al_2(SO_4)_{3(aq)} + 3Cu_{(s)}$$

This is an example of a single displacement reaction, where the aluminum and copper exchange places. The reddish substance that is left over is pure copper. It is very toxic in this form and should not be touched. It should not be poured down the drain, but should be collected in a separate container and taken to a hazardous waste facility. The liquid is aluminum sulfate.

   This experiment can also be done with copper(II) chloride in place of copper(II) sulfate and salt.

Chemical Reactions – Experiment # 12:
REACTION IN A BAG

Objective: To observe the signs that a chemical reaction has taken place.

Materials:
- Quart freezer bag
- Calcium chloride (available in hardware and grocery stores as an ice melter. Sometimes labeled as "Driveway Heat.")
- Baking soda (sodium bicarbonate)
- Red cabbage indicator solution (Prepared by boiling red cabbage leaves in water and pouring out the juice. Universal indicator solution or other acid/base indicators may be substituted.)
- Translucent film canister

Safety Precautions: Do only under adult supervision. Wear safety goggles. Do not point bag toward your eyes. Bag may pop open. Do not shake bag.

Procedure:
1. Place 1 teaspoon each of calcium chloride and baking soda in a freezer bag.
2. Fill the film canister with red cabbage solution and carefully place in the bag without spilling any liquid. Seal the bag shut.
3. Mix the contents by turning over the bag. How many observations can you make?

Explanation: This is a fascinating reaction with surprising results. First the bag will feel hot, then cold. It will expand greatly due to the production of CO_2 gas. The indicator will go through several color changes as a result of a change in pH.

The reaction does not occur until water is added. When solids dissolve in water, their surface area increases greatly, allowing many more molecules to collide and react. The reaction that occurs in the bag is as follows:

$$CaCl_{2(aq)} + 2NaHCO_{3(aq)} \longrightarrow CaCO_{3(aq)} + 2NaCl_{(aq)} + H_2O_{(l)} + CO_{2(g)}$$

The initial heat is formed by the calcium chloride dissolving in water, which is a highly exothermic process. When the calcium chloride then reacts with baking soda, the bag will feel cold, since this is an endothermic reaction. The red cabbage indicator initially turns a pinkish-purple color, due to carbon dioxide gas reacting with water to yield carbonic acid. However, as calcium carbonate ($CaCO_3$) is formed, it neutralizes the carbonic acid, bringing the color of the red cabbage closer to its original color. The final color will vary somewhat, depending on how much of each substance was initially added.

Chemical Reactions – Experiment # 13:
ELECTROLYSIS OF WATER

Objective: To break down water into its constituent elements.

Materials:
- Transparent plastic cups
- 9-V battery
- Distilled water
- Salt (sodium chloride)
- Wood splints (wooden coffee stirrers)

Safety Precautions: Perform only under adult supervision. Wear safety goggles. Hydrogen gas is generated, which is explosive.

Procedure:
1. Place the 9-V battery upright in a clear cup filled with distilled water, so the water just covers the terminals. Observe.
2. Repeat with tap water. Observe carefully.
3. Repeat with salt water. Observe.
4. Bring a flaming wood splint close to the surface of the bubbles collecting at the negative terminal. What happens?

Explanation: When the battery is immersed in the salt water, you should see a copious amount of bubbles being produced at the cathode (negative terminal). You may see a few bubbles in the tap water, and probably none in the distilled water. As we saw in an earlier experiment, salt water is an excellent electrolyte, or conductor of electricity. Pure water is a very poor electrolyte.

The bubbles collecting at the cathode are bubbles of hydrogen gas (H_2). Oxygen (O_2) bubbles collect at the anode (positive terminal). The oxygen bubbles are not as visible because oxygen is much more soluble in water than hydrogen. Also, this particular reaction produces twice the volume of hydrogen gas as oxygen gas. The complete balanced equation is as follows:

$$2H_2O_{(l)} \longrightarrow 2H_{2(g)} + O_{2(g)}$$

The flaming wood splint will produce a slight popping sound when brought near the bubbles produced at the cathode, which verifies that hydrogen gas is being produced. Hydrogen is an explosive gas in the presence of oxygen. The Hindenberg, a famous dirigible, burst into flames in 1937 when this volatile combination ignited. Today, blimps use helium instead of hydrogen, because helium is an inert gas that does not combust.

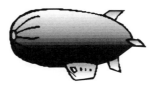

Chemical Reactions – Experiment # 14:
REDUCTION AND OXIDATION OF IODINE

Objective: To observe changes in the color of iodine as it gains and loses electrons.

Materials:
- Galvanized (zinc coated) roofing nails
- Household bleach (5% solution of sodium hypochlorite – NaClO)
- Tincture of iodine (from the drugstore)
- Vinegar (5% solution of acetic acid – CH_3COOH)
- Transparent plastic cups
- Eyedroppers

Safety Precautions: Perform only under adult supervision. Wear safety goggles. Iodine and bleach are both very toxic if ingested. Bleach is extremely caustic to the eyes and skin. Be careful not to spill on clothing.

Procedure:
1. Place about a dozen galvanized roofing nails in the plastic cup.
2. Add just enough tincture of iodine to nearly, but not completely, cover the nails.
3. Pour a little tincture of iodine into a separate cup to serve as a control.
4. After about an hour (or less) pour the liquid covering the nails into a separate cup. It should be a very light yellow color. Compare its color to the unreacted iodine in the control cup.
5. Add a few drops of bleach to the liquid until the color changes back to the original color. Note the cloudiness of the solution.
6. Add vinegar dropwise until the solution is no longer cloudy.

Explanation: The zinc from the nails reacts with the iodine (I_2) in the solution to form the colorless I^- ion. The iodine should change from a reddish brown to a pale yellow color. The reaction is as follows: $Zn + I_2 \longrightarrow Zn^{2+} + 2I^-$
This is an example of an oxidation-reduction (redox) reaction, a chemical reaction that involves the gain and loss of electrons. A substance that gains electrons undergoes reduction, and a substance that loses electrons undergoes oxidation.

   In the above reaction, the zinc has been oxidized, since it has lost 2 electrons. The iodine has been reduced, since each iodine atom has gained an electron. The color change occurs because elemental iodine (I_2) has a deep purple color, whereas the iodide ion (I^-) is colorless. The tincture of iodine is actually more reddish brown than purple because it contains alcohol, which helps to keep the iodine in solution.

When the bleach is added, the pale yellow solution of iodide (I⁻) becomes reddish brown again. This is because the colorless I⁻ has been changed to elemental iodine. The reaction is as follows:

$$2I^- + ClO^- + H_2O \longrightarrow I_2 + Cl^- + 2OH^-$$

Since bleach is a solution of NaClO in water, it supplies the ClO⁻ ion and the H_2O. The colorless I⁻ is oxidized to the colored I_2. Since the ClO⁻ causes the oxidation of the I⁻, the ClO⁻ is referred to as an oxidizing agent, or oxidizer. This is why bleach is such a good cleaning agent – it is a very strong oxidizer.

The final step involves adding vinegar, which causes any clumps or cloudiness in the solution to disappear. These clumps are due to zinc ions (formed in the first reaction) reacting with hydroxide ions (formed in the second reaction). The product is zinc hydroxide. The reaction is as follows:

$$Zn^{2+} + 2OH^- \longrightarrow Zn(OH)_2$$

Since zinc hydroxide ($Zn(OH)_2$) is insoluble in water, it will form a precipitate in the solution, giving it a cloudy appearance. Adding vinegar (CH_3COOH) will break up the insoluble $Zn(OH)_2$ into soluble products, causing the solution to become totally clear. The reaction is as follows:

$$Zn(OH)_2 + 2CH_3COOH \longrightarrow Zn^{2+} + 2H_2O + CH_3COO^-$$

Chemical Reactions – Experiment # 15:
REDUCTION AND OXIDATION OF IODINE: PART 2

Objective: To observe the color changes that accompany the oxidation and reduction of iodine.

Materials:
- Vitamin C tablet
- Tincture of iodine (available from drugstore)
- Household bleach
- Eyedroppers

Safety Precautions: Perform only under adult supervision. Wear safety goggles. Iodine and bleach are both very toxic if ingested. Bleach is extremely caustic to the eyes and skin. Be careful not to spill on clothing.

Procedure:
1. Place a drop of iodine on a vitamin C tablet. Observe the color change over a period of several minutes.
2. Add a drop of bleach to the tablet. Observe the color change for several minutes.

Explanation: The chemical reactions in this experiment are the same as in the previous experiment, except that vitamin C is used in place of zinc. Vitamin C very effectively reduces the colored I_2 molecules to colorless I^- ions. The bleach oxidizes the I^- back to I_2, restoring the color. Eventually, the color will fade as the bleach further oxidizes the I_2 into colorless substances.

Alternately, this experiment can be performed on a larger scale by dissolving vitamin C in water, and then adding iodine and bleach.

Chemical Reactions – Experiment # 16:
CONVERTING STARCH INTO SUGAR

Objective: To convert starch into glucose.

Materials:

- Corn starch
- Tincture of iodine
- Stove or hotplate
- Beaker
- Muriatic acid (available from hardware store)

Safety Precautions: Do only under adult supervision. Wear safety goggles. Muriatic acid is dilute hydrochloric acid, and is extremely corrosive to eyes and skin. Thoroughly read the label on this product before using. Exercise extreme caution when using this substance. Iodine and hydrochloric acid are both toxic if ingested. Do not consume the products of this experiment.

Procedure:

1. Add a teaspoon of corn starch to 100 mL of water in a beaker.
2. Add a few drops of tincture of iodine until a deep blue color forms.
3. Add 10 drops of muriatic acid.
4. Heat and allow to boil for several minutes. Stir occasionally.
5. After the color changes, remove from heat.

Explanation: The blue-black color that initially forms is the result of the starch-iodine complex that forms when iodine reacts with starch. After heating, this color disappears, which shows that the starch has been converted into something else. In this experiment, the starch is converted to glucose, which tests negative with iodine. The hydrochloric acid acts as a catalyst. The equation is as follows:

$$(C_6H_{10}O_5)_x + xH_2O \longrightarrow xC_6H_{12}O_6$$
$$\text{starch} \qquad\qquad\qquad \text{glucose}$$

Starch is a polymer, with many molecules attached together in clusters. That is what the "x" in the above equation represents. One cluster of starch may be composed of any-where from 50 to 1000 molecules. This makes starch an excellent substance for thickening foods, such as gravy or sauces.

The fact that starch can be readily broken down to glucose is very important, since our body uses glucose to provide energy. The conversion of starch into sugar begins with the saliva in your mouth and continues in your stomach, which contains hydrochloric acid.

Chemical Reactions – Experiment # 17:
REMOVING TARNISH FROM SILVER

Objective: To understand the chemical reaction that occurs when tarnish is removed from silver.

Materials:

- Piece of tarnished silver (available from any antique store)
- Beaker or pan (aluminum pans are ideal)
- Aluminum foil
- Baking soda (sodium bicarbonate)
- Salt (sodium chloride)
- Stove or hotplate

Safety Precautions: Perform only under adult supervision. Use potholder to remove silver from pan.

Procedure:
1. Line the beaker or pan with aluminum foil, shiny side up.
2. Fill about halfway with water.
3. Add several tablespoons of baking soda.
4. Add a teaspoon of salt.
5. Add the piece of silver. Try to make sure as much of it as possible comes into contact with the foil.
6. Heat to boiling and allow to boil for 5-10 minutes. If the silver is severely tarnished, you may need to boil for 15-20 minutes. Replace the aluminum foil and baking soda and reheat if all of the tarnish is not removed.

Explanation: Silver becomes tarnished as a result of reacting with hydrogen sulfide (H_2S) and oxygen (O_2) in the air. Hydrogen sulfide is produced naturally by the decomposition of organic matter in the soil. The reaction is as follows:
$$4Ag_{(s)} + 2H_2S_{(g)} + O_{2(g)} \longrightarrow 2Ag_2S_{(s)} + 2H_2O_{(l)}$$
The black tarnish on silver is silver sulfide (Ag_2S.) In this experiment, a single displacement reaction occurs, where the silver and aluminum trade places. The reaction occurs because aluminum has a greater affinity for sulfur than does silver. The reaction is as follows:
$$3Ag_2S_{(s)} + 2Al_{(s)} \longrightarrow 6Ag_{(s)} + Al_2S_{3(aq)}$$
This reaction is known as an electrochemical reaction, which happens when two dissimilar metals are put in contact with one another. An electric current is actually generated between the two metals, which facilitates the transfer of electrons that occur in this reaction. The purpose of the baking soda is to remove the protective aluminum oxide

coating that forms on the surface of the aluminum. This will expose the pure aluminum, causing it to react with the silver. The purpose of the salt is to improve the conductivity of the solution.

This is an excellent example of an oxidation-reduction reaction. When silver tarnishes, it is oxidized, since it loses an electron to gain a 1+ charge. When the tarnish is removed, the silver is reduced, since its charge is reduced from 1+ to 0. The aluminum is therefore oxidized, since its charge is increased from 0 to 3+ by the loss of 3 electrons.

Chemical Reactions – Experiment # 18:
ETCHING A CIRCUIT BOARD

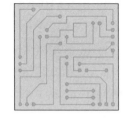

Objective: To observe the reaction between Iron(III) chloride and copper.

Materials:

- PCB Etchant Solution (available from Radio Shack)
- Copper PC Board (available from Radio Shack)
- Shallow plastic tray
- Tongs
- Permanent marker
- Acetone

Safety Precautions: Do only under adult supervision. Wear safety goggles. PCB Etchant Solution contains Iron(III) chloride, or ferric chloride. It is toxic if ingested, and will stain the skin. Acetone is flammable – keep away from flames.

Procedure:
1. Draw a design on the circuit board with the permanent marker.
2. Place the circuit board face down in the plastic tray, and pour the $FeCl_3$ solution to a depth of about G inch. Agitate for 20 minutes.
3. With the tongs, remove the circuit board and rinse with water. Place back in the solution if etching is not complete.
4. Place a little acetone on a paper towel and remove the permanent marker. You should be left with an image of your design in copper.

Explanation: The Iron(III) chloride reacts with the copper, removing any metal not covered with permanent marker. The reaction is as follows:

$$2FeCl_{3(aq)} + Cu_{(s)} \longrightarrow 2FeCl_{2(aq)} + CuCl_{2(aq)}$$

This is an example of an oxidation-reduction reaction, in which the transfer of electrons has occurred. The iron begins as Iron(III) Chloride, which has a 3+ charge. It ends up as Iron(II) Chloride, which has a 2+ charge. Since 2 iron atoms are involved, each takes an electron from a single copper atom, giving the copper a 2+ charge. The iron has been reduced, since it has gained electrons. The copper has been oxidized, since it has lost electrons.

The fact that the above reaction has occurred is evident when the final result is examined. Except for the copper that did not react, there are no solid metals left over. The remaining metals exist only as ions in aqueous solution. If the iron simply traded places with the copper, then there would be a plating of iron on the circuit board where formerly there was copper. This would defeat the entire purpose of etching the board.

Chemical Reactions – Experiment # 19:
EXAMINING A FLAME

Objective: To discover that the inside of a flame is hollow.

Materials:
- Propane torch or Bunsen burner
- 3 x 5 cards
- Container of water
- Tongs

Safety Precautions: Perform only under adult supervision. If the card bursts into flames, dip it in water immediately.

Procedure: 1. Using tongs, hold the card so its face is in the cone of the flame for about a second. Make sure you have a container of water nearby.
2. Quickly remove the card. You should see an unburned area in the center of a charred circle. It may take a little practice to perfect this technique.

Explanation: This experiment vividly shows that the center of a flame is hollow. A flame is basically a region of gases that are reacting quickly with oxygen in the air. These reactions are highly exothermic, releasing both heat and light. In the very center of the flame there is a mixture of unburned gases, which causes the flame to be hollow. In order for the flame to burn, it must react with outside oxygen, which is not present in sufficient quantity in the interior of the flame. This lack of oxygen in the center of the flame creates a region of unburned gases, making the center of the flame hollow.

CHAPTER 9
ACIDS AND BASES

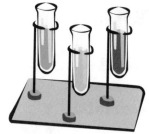

Whether we realize it or not, acids and bases play a major role in our lives. Stomach acid aids in the digestion of food. Sulfuric acid is necessary for the proper operation of an automobile battery. The orange juice we drink for breakfast and the soda we later consume all contain acid. Milk turns sour due to lactic acid. Acids have a pH less than 7 at 25°C.

Soap, detergent, ammonia, bleach, and nearly everything we clean with are examples of bases. Bases taste bitter and tend to feel slippery. Bases have a pH greater than 7 at 25°C.

Chemically speaking, acids produce hydrogen ions (H⁺) in aqueous solution. Bases produce hydroxide ions (OH⁻) in aqueous solution. Acids can also be thought of as proton donors, and bases as proton acceptors.

There are a wide range of fascinating experiments involving acids and bases. A few are presented in this chapter . . .

Acids and Bases – Experiment # 1:
WHY IS MUSTARD YELLOW?

Objective: To discover why mustard has a characteristic yellow color.

Materials:

- Mustard
- Ammonia
- Eyedropper
- Clear plastic cup
- Vinegar

Safety Precautions: Perform this experiment only under adult supervision. Wear safety goggles. Ammonia is very poisonous. Do not eat the mustard after adding ammonia. Do not smell or inhale ammonia fumes.

Procedure:

1. Pour a little mustard in the clear cup. The amount is not crucial.
2. Add ammonia dropwise until you note a color change.
3. Add vinegar dropwise until the mustard returns to its original color.
4. Do not eat the mustard. Dispose by pouring all down the drain.

Explanation: Few people are aware that mustard is yellow due to an additive. If you read the ingredients on the label of a mustard container, it will list turmeric as an ingredient. Turmeric is derived from the root of a plant grown in the East Indies, and is used to dye mustard yellow. It is also an excellent base indicator, turning red in the presence of a base. Since ammonia is basic, mustard will therefore turn red when ammonia is added. When vinegar is added, the ammonia is neutralized, and the turmeric will return to its yellow color.

Turmeric is used to impart the yellow color to goldenrod paper, which also turns red when ammonia or another basic solution is added.

Acids and Bases – Experiment # 2:
ACID/BASE TIE-DYE

Objective: To practice tie-dye technique using a natural acid/base indicator.

Materials:
- White T-shirt
- Head of red cabbage
- Beaker or microwaveable bowl
- Eyedropper
- Ammonia
- Vinegar
- Rubber bands

Safety Precautions: Use microwave only under adult supervision. Exercise caution with boiling water. Ammonia is very poisonous by ingestion or inhalation. Do not inhale fumes. Do not wear shirt when finished.

Procedure:
1. Prepare some red cabbage juice by filling a beaker with red cabbage leaves and then nearly filling with water. Place in the microwave and heat for several minutes. Heat for 2 minutes after water boils. The water should be a deep bluish-purple color. If the water is not very dark, add more leaves and heat again.
2. Pour off the red cabbage juice into a large bowl and allow to cool.
3. Completely submerge the white T-shirt into the cabbage juice.
4. Allow the shirt to dry.
5. Fold the shirt into a typical tie-dye pattern. This can be spiraled, pleated, or folded. Hold the shirt in place with rubber bands.
6. Using an eyedropper, squirt some ammonia on the shirt.
7. Now squirt some vinegar on the shirt.
8. Experiment with other liquids to see if you can produce other colors.
9. Unfold the shirt to reveal the pattern.

Explanation: Red cabbage contains the purple pigment anthocyanin, which is an excellent acid/base indicator. It will turn red in an acid and green in a base, with a variety of intermediate hues. When finished, the shirt can be washed and re-used. This experiment provides a good way to practice your tie-dye technique, especially if you plan on doing real tie-dye in the future, which is permanent.

Acids and Bases – Experiment # 3:
NATURAL ACID/BASE INDICATORS

Objective: To discover the acid/base properties of fruit juices.

Materials:

- Blueberry, cranberry, and grape juice
- Ammonia
- Baking soda
- Laundry detergent
- Vinegar
- Clear plastic cups

Safety Precautions: Perform only under adult supervision. Wear safety goggles. Ammonia and detergent are poisonous. Do not inhale ammonia – fumes are harmful if inhaled. Never drink any substance after chemicals are added.

Procedure:
1. Pour a small amount of blueberry juice into four clear cups.
2. Into the first cup pour a little ammonia. Observe the color change.
3. Into cups 2, 3, and 4, add a little detergent, baking soda, and vinegar, respectively. Observe.
4. Repeat the above steps with the grape and cranberry juice.
5. Try adding additional substances to see if a color change results. Do not drink from any of the cups.

Explanation: The above juices contain a pigment known as anthocyanin, which imparts a deep purple or red color to certain fruits and vegetables. This same pigment is found in red cabbage. Substances which contain anthocyanin are excellent acid/base indicators. When a basic substance, such as ammonia, detergent or baking soda is added to the blueberry juice, it will turn green.   Anthocyanin turns red in the presence of an acid, which is why most of the above juices have a red color already. Depending on its initial color, adding vinegar, an acid, may tend to make the juice a deeper red. Experiment with other fruits and vegetables to determine if they also act as acid/base indicators.

Acids and Bases – Experiment # 4:
DISAPPEARING INK

Objective: To discover how disappearing ink works.

Materials:

- Bottle of disappearing ink (available at magic or novelty stores)
- Clear plastic cups
- Seltzer water (or other acidic liquid such as vinegar or lemon juice)
- Ammonia

Safety Precautions: Disappearing ink is toxic if ingested. Ammonia is also toxic if ingested. Do not inhale ammonia fumes.

Procedure:

1. Squirt some disappearing ink on a white shirt. It will turn clear in a short time.
2. Add a little disappearing ink to a clear cup. Next, add a little seltzer water to the cup. Observe the color change.
3. Add a little ammonia to the same cup. Observe the color change.

Explanation: Disappearing ink is mostly water, with a little thymolphthalein indicator added. A small amount of basic substance is also added, which causes the thymolphthalein to turn a deep blue color. Thymolphthalein is a base indicator, which turns blue in a base and clear in an acid. More specifically, it begins to turn blue at a pH of around 9 or greater, but is clear if the pH is lower than this.

Disappearing ink becomes invisible on your clothes because CO_2 from the air reacts with the water in the solution to form carbonic acid. This lowers the pH, turning the thymolphthalein colorless. The formation of carbonic acid is as follows:

$$CO_{2(g)} + H_2O_{(l)} \longrightarrow H_2CO_{3(aq)}$$

When the seltzer water was added, the thymolphthalein turned clear, because seltzer water contains carbonic acid. When ammonia was added, the carbonic acid was neutralized. This caused the thymolphthalein to turn blue since ammonia is a base.

Acids and Bases – Experiment # 5:
DECOMPOSITION OF BAKING SODA: ANOTHER LOOK

Objective: To discover the acid/base properties of the products of the decomposition of baking soda.

Materials:
- Baking soda (sodium bicarbonate)
- Red cabbage juice (see "Acids and Bases – Experiment # 2")
- Beaker (or substitute)
- Stove or hotplate

Safety Precautions: Do only under adult supervision. Wear safety goggles. Exercise caution when using stove.

Procedure:
1. Fill a beaker halfway with water. Add red cabbage juice (or universal indicator solution if available) until the water is a deep bluish-purple color.
2. Heat for several minutes until near boiling.
3. Slowly add a teaspoon of baking soda. Observe.
4. Slowly add several more teaspoons of baking soda.
5. Stir thoroughly.
6. Continue to heat for several minutes after the water boils.
7. Note the color change.

Explanation: As we saw in "Chemical Reactions – Experiment # 8," the thermal decomposition of baking soda results in the formation of H_2O, CO_2, and Na_2CO_3 (sodium carbonate). The release of CO_2 gas causes the fizzing when it is added to water. As this CO_2 reacts with water, it forms carbonic acid. By itself, this reaction would turn the cabbage indicator red. But there is also a basic product formed – sodium carbonate. This will neutralize any carbonic acid that forms. As the solution is further heated, the carbonic acid will be broken down and the CO_2 gas driven off. Therefore, the remaining sodium carbonate will turn the cabbage indicator green, which signifies a base.

Acids and Bases – Experiment # 6:
ELECTROLYSIS OF WATER: ANOTHER LOOK

Objective: To observe how breaking down water into hydrogen and oxygen affects its pH.

Materials:
- 9-V battery
- Transparent plastic cups
- Red cabbage juice (or universal indicator solution if available)

Safety Precautions: None

Procedure:
1. Place enough red cabbage juice in a cup of tap water to make it a deep bluish-purple solution.
2. Place a 9-V battery in the cup in an upright position. The water level should just cover the top of the terminals.
3. Observe the color changes that result at each terminal.
4. Remove the battery and mix the solution. Observe.

Explanation: This is the same experiment that was performed in "Chemical Reactions – Experiment # 14." If the reaction proceeds too slowly, a pinch of salt can be added to improve conductivity. As an electric current passes through water, it is broken down into hydrogen and oxygen gas. Both of these gases have a neutral pH when added to water. So why then does the red cabbage indicator change color?

To answer this question, it is necessary to examine the reaction in greater detail. There are actually separate reactions occurring at each terminal of the battery. A reduction reaction is occurring at the cathode (negative terminal). H_2 gas is formed here. The reaction is as follows:

$$4H_2O + 4e^- \longrightarrow 2H_2 + 4OH^-$$

From this equation, you can clearly see that hydroxide ions are formed, which cause the red cabbage indicator to turn green. A green color indicates a basic solution, or an abundance of OH^- ions.

An oxidation reaction is occurring at the anode (positive terminal). O_2 gas is produced here. The reaction is as follows:

$$2H_2O \longrightarrow O_2 + 4H^+ + 4e^-$$

From this equation, you can see that hydrogen ions are formed, which cause the red cabbage indicator to turn red. A red color indicates an acidic solution, or an abundance of H^+ ions. It may be more difficult to observe this color change, since the color change produced at the cathode tends to obscure the color change at the anode.

When mixed, the solution becomes neutral again and returns to its original color. Even though there is twice the volume of hydrogen produced as oxygen, the above equations clearly show that the same number of H$^+$ ions are produced as OH$^-$ ions. The H$^+$ will combine with the OH$^-$ to form H$_2$O, which is neutral.

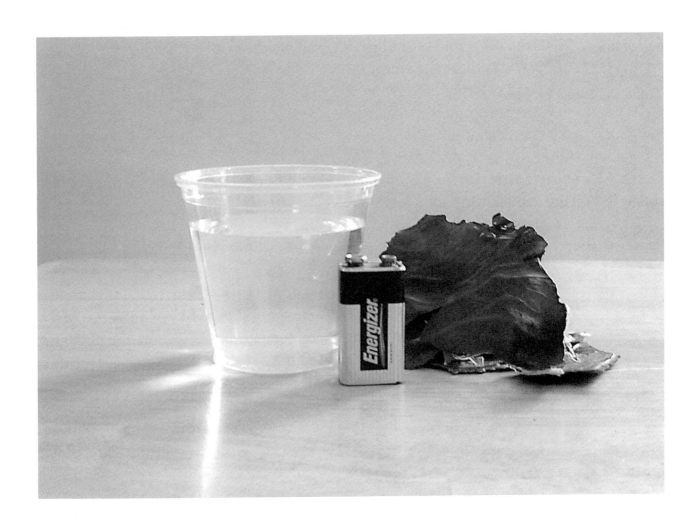

Acids and Bases – Experiment # 7:
MAGIC LEMONS

Objective: To use the acidic nature of lemons to do an intriguing magic trick.

Materials:

- Three lemons
- Hypodermic syringe with needle (available from drug store. If unavailable use a nail and an eyedropper)
- Bromothymol blue indicator (available from a pet or pool supply store)
- Food coloring
- Permanent marker
- Kitchen knife

Safety Precautions: Perform only under adult supervision. Be careful not to prick yourself with the needle. Bromothymol blue is toxic if ingested.

Procedure:

1. Ahead of time, inject a lemon with blue food coloring using the hypodermic needle.
2. Announce to your audience that you will do a magic trick with lemons. Inject another lemon with bromothymol blue indicator solution. Mark the bottom with an X using a permanent marker. Show the audience that the other lemons do not have an X.
3. Change the position of the lemons, challenging your audience to keep their eye on the marked lemon.
4. Ask the audience which lemon was injected with the blue solution. Cut open the lemon that was injected with the bromothymol blue solution. There will be no blue within the lemon!
5. Cut open the untouched lemon and show the audience.
6. Cut open the lemon previously injected with blue food coloring and show the audience.
7. Finally, reveal the location of the X. This should "prove" to your audience that the blue coloring was "magically" transferred to a different lemon.

Explanation: Depending on your audience, you may or may not choose to reveal the secret to this "magic trick." Bromothymol blue is an acid/base indicator. It turns yellow in an acid and is blue in a neutral or basic solution. It will disappear when injected into the lemon, which contains citric acid. You may also experiment with other acid/base indicators if available.

Acids and Bases – Experiment # 8:
HOW THE PIONEERS MADE SOAP

Objective: To discover how to make a concentrated basic solution using only wood ashes and water.

Materials:
- Red cabbage juice (or universal indicator solution)
- Wood ashes
- Transparent plastic cup

Safety Precautions: Perform only under adult supervision. Wear safety goggles. Do not touch the solution formed, as it will be very caustic to the skin and eyes.

Procedure:

1. Add about an inch of wood ashes to a plastic cup.
2. Add the same volume of water to another cup. Add red cabbage juice until it is a deep bluish-purple color.
3. Pour the water into the ashes. Observe the following day.

Explanation: Wood ashes contain potassium oxide (K_2O), which react with water to form potassium hydroxide (KOH). The reaction is as follows:

$$K_2O_{(s)} \ + \ H_2O_{(l)} \ \longrightarrow \ 2KOH_{(aq)}$$

Since potassium hydroxide is strongly basic, it will turn the red cabbage solution a green color.

In the pioneer days, this potassium hydroxide was used to make soap. Rainwater would leach through a barrel filled with wood ashes, and the water that collected would be a solution of potassium hydroxide. To test its concentration, an egg or potato was placed in this solution. If the egg floated, the solution was strong enough to use to make soap. If the egg sank, the solution was not strong enough, and the water would be poured through the ashes again. An alternate method to test the concentration was to drop a feather in the solution. If the feather dissolved, the solution was ready to make soap.

This potassium hydroxide was then mixed with animal fat, heated, and given time to cure. If too much potassium hydroxide was used, it would burn the skin. Perhaps this was why many pioneers bathed so infrequently!

Acids and Bases – Experiment # 9:
MAKE YOUR OWN SOAP

Objective: To create homemade soap.

Materials:
- Sodium hydroxide or lye – NaOH (available in grocery or drug store)
- Ethyl alcohol (available in hardware store as denatured alcohol)
- Salt (sodium chloride)
- Lard
- Heavy duty Pyrex beaker
- Hotplate
- Stirring rod
- Red cabbage juice (or pH paper if available)
- Digital balance
- Measuring cups

Safety Precautions: Do only under adult supervision. You must wear safety goggles and rubber gloves during this entire experiment! Sodium hydroxide is extremely caustic to the skin and eyes. If sodium hydroxide gets in your eyes, flush with water for 15 minutes and call a physician immediately. If it contacts the skin it will first itch and then burn. Wash off with plenty of soap and water if it contacts the skin. Both sodium hydroxide and ethyl alcohol are extremely toxic if ingested. Ethyl alcohol is flammable – remove from work area once you have measured out what you need. Use low heat, or the alcohol in your mixture will burst into flames. If this happens, simply cover with a lid and remove from heat; then turn down heat before proceeding. Do not use soap that you make – it will be too basic and will burn the skin if used. (The purpose of this experiment is to discover how soap can be made, not to produce a useable product.)

Procedure:
1. Place 10 g of NaOH in the beaker.
2. Add 65 mL of water and stir until dissolved.
3. Add 25 mL of ethyl alcohol.
4. Add 30 grams of lard.
5. Heat on low heat on hotplate for 25 minutes. Stir constantly. Be careful not to let the solution boil.
6. Remove from heat. Add 180 mL of water.
7. Heat on hot plate again, until just below boiling.
8. Allow to cool for 5 minutes.
9. Add 30 g of salt. Stir thoroughly.
10. Allow to set overnight.

11. The next day, remove the cake of soap, which will be on top. Be careful not to touch it with your skin. Discard the liquid down the drain.
12. Test the pH of the substance by using pH paper or red cabbage juice. If the red cabbage turns a green or yellow color, this indicates a basic pH.
13. Place a little of the soap in a cup and see if you can make suds by adding a little water and stirring.
14. Put in a safe place where it will be undisturbed for 4 weeks. Test the pH again after this time.

Explanation: The production of soap using the above method is known as saponification. The reaction is as follows:

Fat + sodium hydroxide ⟶ Soap + glycerol

Soap is the sodium salt of a long-chain fatty acid. During the above reaction, part of the fat (or triglyceride) molecule combines with 3 sodium ions from the sodium hydroxide. The hydroxide ions from the sodium hydroxide combine with the other part of the fat molecule to form glycerol.

The purpose of the alcohol is to help the sodium hydroxide and lard to react, by increasing the solubility of the lard in the sodium hydroxide solution. The salt, which is added at the end, decreases the solubility of the soap in the solution, causing it to separate out.

A small amount of soap suds should form when the soap is added to water and stirred. The pH will probably be around 11 or 12, much too high to be used on the skin. After curing for several weeks, the pH will tend to decrease somewhat.

CHAPTER 10
POLYMERS

Polymers are everywhere. Garbage bags, Styrofoam cups, milk jugs, toothpaste tubes, shoe strings, pop bottles, sandwich bags, egg cartons, thread spools, diapers, insulation, caulking, shrink wrap, bubble wrap, Silly String, Silly Putty, Slime, Super Glue, Teflon, toothbrushes, combs, carpet, telephones, floor tile, rubber soles, tires, sunglasses, contact lenses, panty hose, umbrellas, Nerf balls, Frisbees, wet suits, volleyballs, racquetballs, tennis balls, tennis racquets, guitar strings, balloons, rubber bands, credit cards, computers, false teeth, hearing aids, lunch trays, lawn chairs, Astroturf, Velcro, Spandex, footballs, hockey pucks, buttons, erasers, wigs, surfboards, parachutes, sailboats, playing cards, clarinets, flutes, records, videotapes, computer discs, luggage, flea collars, life rafts, pacifiers, baby bottles, photographic film, mannequins, book bags, bowling balls, knapsacks, fishing line, vitamin capsules, sponges, tents, windshield wipers, bubble-gum, tents, house paint, toilet seats, Creepy Crawlers, cameras, polyester, bulletproof vests, Band-Aids, rain coats, flags, and puppets are all made from polymers.

What is a polymer? A polymer is a giant molecule composed of many repeating units known as monomers. The prefix poly- means many. Each monomer within a polymer may be identical, or they may be different. A single polymer molecule may be composed of thousands of monomers that are bonded together.
Polymers may be natural, such as starch, proteins, cellulose, and rubber from rubber trees. Plastics, synthetic rubber, and nylon are examples of manmade polymers.

You will begin to explore the wonderful world of polymers in the following chapter . . .

Polymers – Experiment # 1:
POLYVINYL ALCOHOL SLIME

Objective: To manufacture your own slime.

Materials:

- Elmer's Glue Gel (or a comparable blue glue gel)
- 20 Mule Team Borax (available from the grocery store)
- 2-Liter bottle
- Eyedropper
- Disposable plastic cup
- Popsicle stick
- Food coloring (optional)

Safety Precautions: Borax is poisonous if ingested and is an eye irritant. Wear safety goggles while performing this experiment. Keep the slime out of reach of small children.

Procedure:
1. Add 1 cup of the powdered borax to a 2-Liter bottle of water. Shake vigorously for about 10 minutes. This will be the saturated borax solution.
2. Add some Elmer's Gel Glue to a plastic cup. Add as much or as little as you would like.
3. Add as much water as glue, and stir thoroughly. You will now have a 50:50 mixture of glue and water. At this point, you may add a few drops of food coloring if you wish.
4. Add the saturated borax solution a few drops at a time with an eye-dropper until the slime forms on your stick.
5. Add the borax solution until most of the glue has been turned into slime. Be careful not to add too much borax, or it will be too stiff. A good rule of thumb is to make sure there is always a little liquid left in the bottom of the cup when finished. This way you know you have not added too much borax.
6. Remove with your fingers and work it with your hands.
7. Rinse under water.
8. Store in an airtight plastic bag.

Explanation: Elmer's Glue Gel is an example of a thixotropic gel. This is a substance where the viscosity changes when the molecules are disrupted. If the substance is disturbed, it becomes less viscous (more runny). Thus when the glue bottle is squeezed, it acts more like a liquid and flows out of the bottle. When at rest, it acts more like a solid.

Elmer's Glue Gel is a solution of polyvinyl alcohol in water. The glue also contains many other additives in small amounts. These polyvinyl alcohol molecules tend to slide past one another fairly easily. When the borax is added, it causes the polyvinyl alcohol molecules to become crosslinked. This gives the material its unique slimy texture. You can think of crosslinking as railroad ties which link together two rails – the ties hold the rails in place.

Polymers – Experiment # 2:
GHOST CRYSTALS

Objective: To discover the properties of a super-absorbent gel.

Materials:
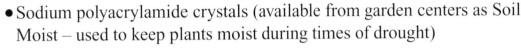
- Sodium polyacrylamide crystals (available from garden centers as Soil Moist – used to keep plants moist during times of drought)
- Quart freezer bag
- Thread

Safety Precautions: Sodium polyacrylamide crystals are harmless to the touch, but are harmful if swallowed. Keep out of reach of small children. Do not pour down drain.

Procedure:
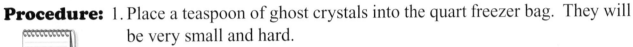
1. Place a teaspoon of ghost crystals into the quart freezer bag. They will be very small and hard.
2. Add 3 cups of water.
3. After an hour or so observe the crystals.
4. Remove a few crystals and place in a clear cup of water. Observe.
5. Make a loop with a piece of thread and suspend in water. Observe.
6. Stick a toothpick through the crystal and submerge in water. Observe.
7. Repeat using colored water. What happens?
8. Remove a crystal and add salt. What happens?

Explanation: Ghost crystals receive their name from the fact that they appear invisible underwater. This is because they have the same index of refraction as water. In other words, these crystals bend or refract light just as much as water. As a result, they appear invisible in water.

These crystals have a wide variety of uses. They are commonly sold in garden centers as a way to prevent plants from suffering water loss during a drought. If placed in the soil and watered, they will release this water gradually to the soil during times of drought. They are also used in head bands to absorb water. As this water gradually evaporates, your skin is cooled. They are even utilized in bath gels and as a medium to store crickets for pet food. They have also been used to draw water from fuel tanks.

Ghost crystals are an example of a super-absorbent polymer that can absorb up to 500 times their own weight in water. They are similar in composition to the sodium polyacrylate polymer used in baby diapers. You can calculate how much water they absorb by weighing a crystal before and then after water is added. The ghost crystals absorb more distilled water than tap water.

Adding salt will shrink the size of the crystal. This is because water will tend to leave the crystal through osmosis in an attempt to dilute the salt on the outside. A similar process is used to convert cucumbers into pickles.

Polymers – Experiment # 3:
POLYMER WORMS

Objective: To make polymer "worms" due to cross-linking of polymer chains.

Materials:

- Gaviscon liquid antacid (available from the drug store)
- Calcium chloride (available from hardware and grocery stores as an ice melter. Sometimes labeled as "Driveway Heat")
- Popsicle stick for stirring
- Clear plastic cup or beaker

Safety Precautions: Wear safety goggles when doing this experiment. Calcium Chloride is poisonous and will cause eye irritation. Gaviscon antacid should be kept out of reach of small children.

Procedure:

1. Prepare an aqueous solution of calcium chloride by adding a teaspoon of calcium chloride to a cup of water. Stir until all is dissolved. (A 1% solution is sufficient.)
2. Slowly pour a little Gaviscon into the calcium chloride solution. Observe.

Explanation: Sodium alginate is a very common food additive. It is used as a thickener in ice cream, Cheez Whiz, Nutri-Grain bars, and a host of other substances. Gaviscon antacid also contains sodium alginate. When poured into the calcium chloride solution, the sodium ions trade places with the calcium ions. As a result, the polymer chains of the alginate become crosslinked, resulting in the formation of the polymer "worms." Crosslinking causes the polymer to become rigid. If the "worms" are allowed to remain in solution, they will become much more rigid.

The calcium ions are able to cause crosslinking because each calcium ion has a 2+ charge, which is able to bond to a 1- charge on two separate polymer chains. The sodium ion, on the other hand, only has a 1+ charge, so it is not able to connect two separate chains.

Polymers – Experiment # 4:
TESTING FRUIT DRINKS FOR CALCIUM

Objective: To determine if a fruit drink contains calcium.

Materials:
- Gaviscon liquid antacid
- Cranberry fruit drink without calcium
- Cranberry fruit drink with calcium
- Two clear plastic cups or beakers

Safety Precautions: Do not drink the products of this experiment.

Procedure: 1. Pour a little of each drink into two separate cups.
2. Add a little Gaviscon antacid to each. Observe.

Explanation: The Gaviscon will form polymer "worms" in the drink with the calcium, but will not in the drink without the calcium. As we saw in the last experiment, calcium ions will cause the alginate polymer chains in the Gaviscon to crosslink and form polymer "worms." This happens in the fruit drink that is fortified with calcium. In the drink without calcium, no crosslinking occurs. This is an excellent test to see if a drink actually contains calcium ions.

Interestingly, if Gaviscon is added to milk, the polymer "worms" do not form. Even though milk contains calcium, the calcium does not exist as free ions. Test other food substances with Gaviscon to see if they too contain calcium ions.

Polymers – Experiment # 5:
METAMUCIL SLIME

Objective: To create slime using Metamucil.

Materials:
- Metamucil (available in the drug store)
- Beaker or microwaveable cup
- Microwave oven
- Oven mitts

Safety Precautions: Perform this experiment only under adult supervision. The slime produced in this experiment will be very, very hot! Use potholders or insulated gloves when handling the beaker. Do not handle slime until after it cools.

Procedure:
1. Place about a teaspoon of Metamucil in a large beaker or other microwaveable glassware.
2. Add about 250 mL of water, and stir. If desired, food coloring can be added.
3. Heat in the microwave for about 5 minutes, but keep a close watch on it. It will begin to boil and then to rise. If it looks like it will spill out of the container, turn off the microwave and allow it to cool.
4. Repeat this process 6 times, allowing it to cool for 5 minutes between each heating. Heat until it begins to rise. It will be very hot at this point, so exercise caution.
5. Allow to cool for an hour or so before touching. When cool, remove it from the beaker. You have created your own microwaveable slime! Store in an airtight bag. Keep in the refrigerator. If mold develops on the slime, discard it.

Explanation: Metamucil is 95% fiber. Fiber is composed of complex carbohydrates that differ from sugar and starch in that our bodies lack the necessary enzymes to digest it. But fiber is an important part of our diet, and aids in digestion and the removal of waste from the body.

When added to water and heated, fiber molecules form hydrogen bonds with the water molecules, causing a gelatinous mass to be produced. As the particles of fiber absorb water molecules, they swell up. The Metamucil slime you created is a good example of a gel, which is a colloidal suspension where a liquid is dispersed in a solid.

Polymers – Experiment # 6:
MAKE YOUR OWN PLAY DOUGH

Objective: To observe the effect of heating starch in water.

Materials:

- 1 cup flour
- 1 cup water
- 1 teaspoon vegetable oil
- 2 teaspoons cream of tartar
- 1/4 cup salt
- Food coloring
- Pan or beaker
- Heat source

Safety Precautions: Perform only under adult supervision. Exercise caution when using stove.

Procedure:
1. Add the above ingredients to a pan. Stir thoroughly, until the mixture is free of all clumps.
2. Heat over medium heat for about 3 minutes or until the mixture begins to thicken.
3. Remove from heat. When cool, knead into desired consistency.
4. Store in an airtight bag.

Explanation: When heated, starch undergoes gelatinization, or thickening. This is due to hydrogen bonding between the starch and water molecules. The granules of starch absorb water and swell up. The starch granules become a tangled, amorphous network, losing all structure. This gives the play dough its unique texture. Play dough is actually an example of a gel. A gel is a colloid where a liquid is suspended in a solid. Other examples of gels are jelly and gelatin.

Polymers – Experiment # 7:
SHRINKY DINKS

Objective: To discover the effect of heat on polystyrene.

Materials:

- Piece of clear polystyrene plastic. (Obtain from the top of a Dannon yogurt container or a salad container – will have a recycling code of "6")
- Oven
- Permanent Marker
- Cookie sheet

Safety Precautions: Do only under adult supervision. Use a potholder when taking cookie sheet from oven. Do not touch plastic until it has cooled.

Procedure:

1. If using the top of a yogurt container, remove the colored strip from the edge. Otherwise cut out a square piece of plastic. Draw a design on the plastic with a permanent marker.
2. If desired, punch a hole in the plastic with a hole puncher, so it may be attached to a key chain when finished.
3. Place on a cookie sheet and put in the oven for about 5 minutes at 350°F (170°C).

Explanation: If you have ever thrown a Styrofoam cup into a campfire, you know that Styrofoam shrinks considerably when heated If a 2-Liter bottle is filled with boiling water, it will noticeably shrink in size. Many packages are shrink-wrapped in plastic. Certain types of plastics that are put over windows in the winter for insulation must be shrink-fitted with a hair dryer. Polystyrene, which is used in this experiment, also shrinks when heated. The reason for this can be traced back to its manufacture.

In order to be made into a film, the polystyrene must be heated, stretched, and then quickly cooled. This locks the plastic into a particular shape and thickness. When heated again, it becomes unlocked, and returns to its original position and thickness.

Experiment with plastic plates and cups that are also made of polystyrene. Heat them in the oven using the same procedure as above. What happens?

CHAPTER 11
ENERGY

Energy is difficult to define. We all know what it means to lack energy, or to have energy, but just what is energy? Energy has often been defined as the ability to do work or raise the temperature of an object.

You don't really have to do anything to have energy, since energy can be stored to use as needed. Stored energy is referred to as potential energy. Fuel, food, a wound-up alarm clock, a compressed spring, or a rock on top of a hill all contain potential energy.

Kinetic energy refers to energy of motion. Any moving object possesses kinetic energy. You can also refer to the internal kinetic energy that every object above absolute zero (O K) contains. Internal kinetic energy is energy due to the motion of molecules within a substance. An object's temperature is a measure of its internal kinetic energy.

In this chapter, we will attempt to shed some light on the mostly unseen world of energy . . .

Energy – Experiment # 1:
TESTING FOOD FOR CALORIES

Objective: To determine the relative energy content of different foods by burning.

Materials:

- Alligator clip (available from Radio Shack)
- Small block of wood
- Nail
- Hammer
- Pliers
- Matches or lighter
- Various types of snack food, such as peanuts, potato chips, pretzels, Fritos, nachos, etc.

Safety Precautions: Do only under adult supervision. This experiment will generate smoke, so only do outdoors or in a well-ventilated area. Exercise caution when using matches. The metal clip will be very hot after burning – do not touch unless first cooling it with water.

Procedure:
1. Drive a small headless nail into a small block of wood.
2. Place the alligator clip over the nail and crimp tightly with pliers so that it remains in place.
3. Place a single food item (such as a potato chip) in the clip.
4. Light the item from the bottom, until it burns on its own.
5. Record the amount of time it takes various food items to burn. Also note the size of the flame for each item. Use these criteria to determine which foods release the most energy when burned.

Explanation: Surprisingly, many foods burn remarkably well. This is because all foods contain potential energy, or stored energy, which is released upon burning or during digestion within our bodies. Different types of food contain more energy than others. The amount of energy a certain type of food contains is measured by how many Calories that food contains. Different types of nutrients contain differing amounts of Calories. Proteins and carbohydrates (starches and sugars) both contain 4 Calories per gram. Fat, on the other hand, contains 9 Calories per gram. Therefore, foods with a high fat content will burn very well, since fat contains much more energy than protein or carbohydrates. Most of our snack foods are high in fat content, and thus burn very well. A food with little fat, such as pretzels, will not burn well at all.

It should be noted that what we commonly refer to as calories (with a small c) are actually Calories (with a capital C). Food labels always list the energy content of foods in

Calories, which are actually kilocalories. A kilocalorie, or Calorie (capital C), is actually 1000 calories (small c). So if you consume a candy bar that contains 300 Calories, it is more accurate to say that you have consumed 300 kilocalories, or 300,000 calories. A typical person, therefore, will actually consume 2 to 3 million calories per day!

A calorie is defined as the amount of energy required to raise the temperature of 1 gram of water by 1 degree C. The caloric content of different foods is calculated this way. By burning foods in a specially constructed device known as a calorimeter, the exact amount of energy that each food contains can be calculated.

Energy – Experiment # 2:
A QUICK WAY TO THAW FOODS

Objective: To discover whether commercially available defrosting trays really work.

Materials:
- Defrost Wonder or Miracle Thaw defrosting tray (available from department stores. A black aluminum pan will suffice if the above is not available.)
- Ice cubes

Safety Precautions: None

Procedure:
1. Place an ice cube on the Defrost Wonder tray. At the same time place another ice cube on the table or countertop.
2. Record the time it takes for each to melt.

Explanation: The Defrost Wonder does indeed work as advertised. It will melt ice much more quickly than will the tabletop or countertop. The key to this seemingly miraculous device is the fact that it is made from aluminum, which possesses some interesting properties. First of all, aluminum has a relatively high heat capacity for a metal. It has the potential to store a great deal of energy. When the aluminum is cooled, this energy is released, melting ice or thawing frozen foods. But this is only part of the picture. The Defrost Wonder is also effective because aluminum is an excellent conductor. Good conductors can transfer energy quickly. Aluminum, which can hold a good deal of energy, can release this energy very quickly, making it extremely effective at thawing foods rapidly. The fact that it is painted black also helps, since black absorbs all wavelengths of visible light, therefore causing the Defrost Wonder to have more energy available to be released when cooled. It is not really necessary to spend $20.00 on this device in order to benefit from the chemistry involved. Any black aluminum pan will achieve nearly the same effect.

This same principle has many practical applications. Metal bleachers always feel colder than wood or plastic, because metal conducts heat away from your body much more quickly than does wood or plastic. When stirring a pot of boiling water, a wooden or plastic spoon should be used, since a metal spoon will get hot. This is because metals are much better conductors of heat than wood or plastic.

Energy – Experiment # 3:
FALLING THUMBTACKS

Objective: To demonstrate the conduction of heat by metals.

Materials:

- 2 – 3 foot long metal rod or pipe (available from hardware store)
- Metal flat-headed thumbtacks
- Paraffin wax (available from grocery store)
- Propane torch
- Vise or clamp
- Pliers or tongs

Safety Precautions: Perform only under adult supervision. Wear safety goggles. Be careful when using propane torch. Do not touch the metal rod or paraffin after it is heated.

Procedure:
1. Melt a small amount of wax in a pan over the stove.
2. Using tongs, grip a thumbtack by its point and submerge it in the melted wax.
3. Quickly place the thumbtack on the metal rod, close to the end.
4. Repeat with other thumbtacks. Place each about an inch apart until the entire length of the rod is covered. Be sure to place the tacks in a straight line.
5. After the wax has hardened, invert the rod and place in a vise, or otherwise support the rod so it is horizontal with the tacks facing downward.
6. Place a propane torch under one end of the rod and heat it strongly.
7. Observe what happens to the thumbtacks.

Explanation: Metals are excellent conductors of heat due to the fact that their atoms are packed very close together. This gives metals a relatively high density. Conduction is the transfer of energy by direct contact. If you were to touch a hot stove, energy would travel into your hand by the process of conduction. When the metal rod is heated, energy is transferred from one metal atom to the next. This transfer of energy is analogous to a billiard ball striking another ball and transferring some of its energy to that ball. Eventually, energy will be transferred down the entire length of the rod due to conduction. This is evidenced by the fact that the thumbtacks will gradually fall off one by one as the rod becomes warmer and melts the wax. If you are patient, eventually every thumbtack will fall off!

Energy – Experiment # 4:
ARE HEAT AND TEMPERATURE THE SAME THING?

Objective: To discover the difference between heat and temperature.

Materials:
- Three dishpans or large bowls
- Ice cubes
- Hot water

Safety Precautions: Make sure the hot water is not so hot that it burns you. Test quickly with your finger before performing this experiment.

Procedure:

1. Fill one dishpan about halfway with room temperature water.
2. Fill the second dishpan about halfway with very hot tap water, but not so hot as to burn you.
3. Fill the third dishpan about halfway with ice water by adding a tray of ice cubes to cold water.
4. Submerge one hand in the hot water for one minute. Then immediately submerge the same hand in the room temperature water.
5. Next, submerge the same hand in the ice water for one minute. Then immediately submerge the same hand in the room temperature water.
6. Finally, submerge one hand in hot water and the other in cold water for one minute. Then immediately submerge both hands in the room temperature water.

Explanation: This is a classic experiment that clearly shows that hot and cold is simply a matter of perception. There is really no such thing as cold, but only heat and the absence of heat. Heat is actually defined as energy that is being transferred from one object to another. It is more accurate to say that something contains a certain amount of energy rather than heat, since this energy only becomes heat when it is moving from one substance to another.

Energy always travels from a substance with high energy to one with low energy. Balls always roll downhill spontaneously. They are moving from a position of high potential energy to a position of low potential energy. In the same way, energy always flows from hot to cold. If you touch a hot stove, energy travels into your hand and you get burned. If you touch a piece of ice, energy leaves your hand and travels into the ice; therefore your hand feels cold.

The hot water feels hot because energy is traveling from the water to your hand. When you immediately place your hot hand into room temperature water, energy travels from your hand into the water. Therefore your hand feels cold. When you later place your ice cold hand into the room temperature water, it feels warm because now energy travels from the water into your hand. So even though the room temperature water was the same temperature both times, it feels cold one time and hot the next.

When both a hot and cold hand are placed into the room temperature water simultaneously, you may feel any of a number of sensations. Your brain is receiving conflicting signals so it becomes temporarily confused. You may feel alternating hot and cold sensations for either hand.

This experiment clearly shows that heat and temperature are two very different things. Temperature is a measure of how fast the molecules within a substance are moving. It can be directly measured with a thermometer. Heat, on the other hand, cannot be measured directly; we can only determine when it is leaving or arriving.

CHAPTER 12
ELECTRICITY
AND
MAGNETISM

Electricity and magnetism are intimately related. They both arise from the same fundamental force – the electromagnetic force. The electricity that powers your home is produced by a generator within a power plant. A generator works by rotating many coils of wire within a magnetic field, which in turn produces electricity. Were it not for magnetism, we would not have electricity.

The electromagnetic force is also responsible for all of the interactions between charged particles. This can range from static electricity to the bonds that form compounds. The fact that like charges repel and opposite charges attract is due to the electromagnetic force.

In this chapter, we will examine electricity and magnetism from a chemical perspective. The branch of chemistry that deals with electricity is electrochemistry, which we will touch upon in this chapter . . .

Electricity and Magnetism – Experiment # 1:
DEMONSTRATING THE IONIC NATURE OF SALT

Objective: To demonstrate that salt contains both positive and negative charges.

Materials:
- Balloon
- Table salt

Safety Precautions: None

Procedure:
1. Sprinkle some table salt on a tabletop.
2. Rub an inflated balloon vigorously in your hair. Your hair must be clean and dry. (In lieu of hair, a wool sweater may be used.)
3. Gradually bring the balloon close to the granules of salt.

Explanation: As you rub the balloon vigorously in your hair, some electrons are transferred from your hair to the balloon. This is because the balloon has a greater affinity (attraction) for electrons than does hair. As a result, the balloon is now negatively charged, since it has an excess of electrons. Your hair is positively charged, since it has a deficiency of electrons. This is why your hair will tend to stand on end after rubbing with the balloon. Since your hairs are now positively charged, they will repel one another. It is for this reason that a person's hair will stand on end immediately before being struck by lightning! Like charges repel; opposite charges attract.

Table salt is an example of an ionic compound, which means that it is composed of ions. An ion is an atom that has a charge. A positive ion, or cation, has lost an electron(s). A negative ion, or anion, has gained an electron(s). Sodium chloride is composed of positive sodium ions and negative chloride ions. These ions are attracted to one another, forming sodium chloride.

When the negatively charged balloon is brought toward the granules of sodium chloride, they are attracted to the balloon since salt contains many positive charges. It is these positive charges within the salt that make it stick to the balloon. The negative charges in the salt are repelled by the balloon, so they will tend to be deflected away. If you look closely, you can see the little salt granules flipping around to orient themselves in such a way as to have the maximum number of positive charges toward the balloon and the maximum number of negative charges away from the balloon.

Electricity and Magnetism – Experiment # 2:
BENDING WATER

Objective: To discover why a stream of water can be deflected by a charged object.

Materials: • Faucet
• Balloon

Safety Precautions: None

Procedure: 1. Run a small stream of water under the faucet. If a faucet is unavailable, poke a small hole in a 2-Liter bottle of water to make a stream of water.
2. Rub the balloon vigorously in your hair and bring it close to, but not touching, the stream of water. (Your hair must be clean and dry.) Observe the behavior of the water.

Explanation: The stream of water should be noticeably deflected by the charged balloon. As we saw in the last experiment, rubbing the balloon against your hair transfers electrons from your hair to the balloon. This causes the balloon to become negatively charged. Water is a polar molecule, containing both positive and negative charges. The negative charges are repelled by the negatively charged balloon, and the positive charges are attracted to the balloon. This is why the stream of water is attracted to the balloon.

It should be mentioned that nonpolar substances can also be attracted to a charged balloon. It is not so much the polar nature of water that is responsible for this effect, but rather that water contains mobile charges that can be easily moved around. Nonpolar substances also contain positive and negative charges, but these charges are evenly distributed. When approached by a negatively charged object, the positives are attracted and the negatives are repelled. It should rather be said that any liquid that is able to be polarized will be attracted to a charged object, and not just polar liquids.

Electricity and Magnetism – Experiment # 3:
A SIMPLE ELECTROMAGNET

Objective: To discover that an electrical field can produce a magnetic field.

Materials:

- Iron nail or bolt
- Insulated bell wire (buy from Radio Shack)
- 6-V lantern battery
- Wire stripper
- Paperclips

Safety Precautions: Do not leave your electromagnet connected when not in use – it will drain the battery and become very hot.

Procedure:
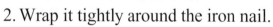
1. Obtain a length of bell wire about 2 feet long, and strip off an inch of insulation from each end.
2. Wrap it tightly around the iron nail.
3. Connect both ends of the exposed wire to the battery terminals.
4. Pick up a paperclip with the end of the nail, which is now magnetized.

Explanation: Electricity, whether it be DC or AC, is the flow of electrons. If these electrons flow in a coil, a magnetic field is produced. This is why the iron nail is able to pick up a paperclip. This experiment clearly shows the relationship between magnetism and electricity. They are actually due to the same force – the electromagnetic force. A moving magnetic field will give rise to an electrical field, just as an electrical field that travels in a coil will give rise to a magnetic field.

Electricity and Magnetism – Experiment # 4:
HOW TO CANCEL OUT A MAGNETIC FIELD

Objective: To discover what causes magnetism.

Materials:

- Bell wire
- Iron nail or bolt
- Wire stripper
- Two 6-V lantern batteries
- Paperclips

Safety Precautions: Do not leave wires connected to batteries when not in use – this will cause the batteries to become very hot and also cause them to run down.

Procedure:
1. Wrap one strand of bell wire tightly around an iron nail. Leave several inches of unwrapped wire at each end of the nail.
2. Wrap another piece of wire in the opposite direction around the first piece of wire. Make sure this wire is wrapped directly over the first piece, and that there is the same number of loops in each wire. Leave several inches of wire unwrapped at each end.
3. Attach the two ends of the wire at one side of the nail to the positive terminals of two batteries. (see illustration on following page)
4. Attach the two ends of the wire at the other side of the nail to the negative terminals of two batteries.
5. Now attempt to pick up a magnet with the nail.

Explanation: The electromagnet you constructed in the previous experiment was able to pick up a paperclip, but this experiment reveals that wrapping another wire in the opposite direction around the first one will cancel out the magnetic field. If the magnetic field was not cancelled out, it is probably because the other wire was not wrapped in the opposite direction, the number of loops was not the same, or the batteries were of unequal strength.

A magnetic field is caused by electrons spinning about rapidly within the orbitals of an atom. An orbital is a region of space outside of the nucleus where electrons are most likely to be found. Some orbitals contain only one electron. The three elements which are strongly attracted to a magnet at room temperature – iron, cobalt, and nickel – each contain some orbitals that have only one electron. All of these single electrons within these orbitals spin in the same direction. The spinning of these unpaired electrons in the same direction is what produces a magnetic field in these elements, causing them to be strongly attracted to a magnet. Elements which are strongly attracted to a magnet are termed ferromagnetic.

Metals that are not magnetic, such as copper, tin, and aluminum, all have orbitals which contain two electrons. The electrons within these orbitals are spinning in opposite directions, which cancel out the other's magnetic field. Elements which are not attracted to a magnet are termed diamagnetic.

The electromagnet you constructed in the previous experiment demonstrates why some elements are ferromagnetic. Just as electrons within an orbital spinning in one direction create a magnetic field, so does a flow of electrons through a wire coiled in one direction. In the experiment you just performed, the two wires wrapped in opposite directions cancelled out each other's magnetic field, just as two electrons spinning within an orbital cancels out each other's magnetic field. Just remember: electrons spinning in one direction create a magnetic field. Another electron spinning in the opposite direction will cancel out this magnetic field. This holds true both for individual atoms and for electromagnets.

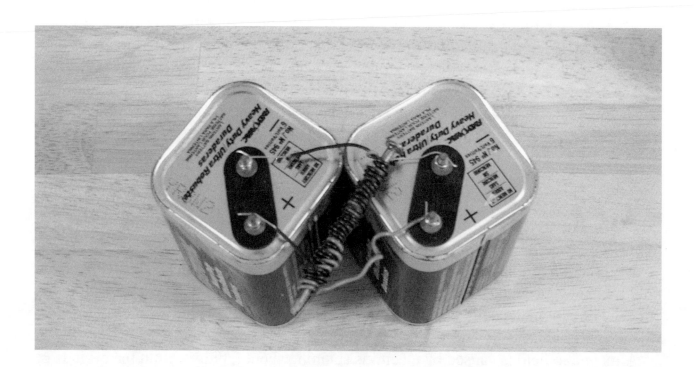

Electricity and Magnetism – Experiment # 5:
THE CURIE POINT

Objective: To determine the effect of temperature on an object's magnetic field.

Materials:
- Canadian nickel (minted before 1982)
- Propane torch
- Metal tongs
- Magnet

Safety Precautions: Perform only under adult supervision. Exercise caution when using propane torch. Do not touch the nickel after it is heated.

Procedure:
1. Using the metal tongs, hold the magnet with the nickel attached under the flame of the propane torch.
2. Heat the nickel strongly until it falls off. After the nickel cools, try attracting it again with the magnet.

Explanation: Canadian nickels (minted before 1982), as well as other Canadian coins, are composed primarily of nickel. Nickel is a ferromagnetic element, which means it is strongly attracted to a magnet. The nickel will no longer be attracted to a magnet when it is heated to a certain temperature. The temperature at which a substance loses its magnetic properties is known as the Curie Point. For nickel, it is 350°C. For iron, it is 800°C. (Try this same experiment with a piece of iron to see if your torch can heat to that temperature.)

Substances can lose their magnetic properties if the domains within a magnet become random and unaligned. A domain is a region within a substance where the atoms tend to be aligned in the same direction. Since a single domain is never more than about 1 mm. long or wide, there are many orbitals within a single domain. These unpaired electrons which are all spinning in the same direction within each orbital give rise to a magnetic field. Heating changes this orientation, because as the temperature rises the atoms begin moving about haphazardly, causing the domains to no longer line up. When the nickel cools, the atoms line up in the same fashion as before, and become attracted to the magnet once again.

Electricity and Magnetism – Experiment # 6:
DISTORTION OF A TV IMAGE

Objective: To observe the deflection of electrons by a magnetic field.

Materials:
- Old television set
- Powerful magnet (preferably a neodymium magnet)

Safety Precautions: Perform this experiment only under adult supervision. Do this experiment only on an old television. It may cause permanent damage to the television set.

Procedure: Run the magnet over the television screen while it is playing. Note the effect it has on the image.

Explanation: This amazing experiment clearly shows the deflection of electrons by a magnetic field. The image will be very visibly distorted in the direction of the magnet. The picture tube in a television set is actually a cathode ray tube, which shoots beams of electrons toward the screen. These beams of electrons illuminate the phosphor coating on the inside of the screen, thus creating a picture. Since electrons are deflected by a magnetic field, the image is distorted when a magnet is brought near. Really wild effects can be created using a color television screen, but the long term effects on the television set are probably not good.

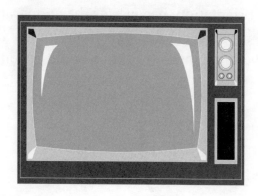

Electricity and Magnetism – Experiment # 7:
EDDY CURRENTS

Objective: To demonstrate that a moving magnetic field will generate an electrical field.

Materials:
- Four foot long copper pipe (available from hardware store – make sure its diameter is just large enough for a magnet to pass through)
- Powerful magnet
- Quarter (or other coin)

Safety Precautions: None

Procedure:
1. Hold the copper pipe upright and drop the quarter through the pipe. Note its rate of fall.
2. Now drop the magnet through the pipe and note its rate of fall.
3. Try holding the pipe at various angles and drop the magnet through the pipe.

Explanation: The magnet is clearly not attracted to the copper pipe, so this experiment poses an interesting dilemma. Why does the quarter fall through the pipe so much faster than the magnet? A fascinating phenomenon is at work here. As the magnet moves through the pipe, it creates an electrical current in the metal, known as an eddy current. Any moving magnetic field will create an electrical current. These currents in turn create a magnetic field, which repels the magnetic field of the magnet as it moves down the pipe. This is what slows the magnet down. The magnet still falls due to gravity. The magnetic field generated by the eddy currents is not strong enough to stop the magnet completely. You can also rub the magnet along the outside of the copper pipe to feel the effects of the eddy currents.

Electricity and Magnetism – Experiment # 8:
REMOVING IRON FROM CEREAL

Objective: To remove elemental iron filings from breakfast cereal.

Materials:

- Total cereal
- Bowl
- Spoon
- Magnet (preferably painted white)

Safety Precautions: None

Procedure:

1. Pour some Total cereal flakes into a bowl.
2. Add just enough water to cover the flakes.
3. Break up the flakes with the spoon until a slurry is formed.
4. With a circular motion, stir the cereal with the magnet for about 10 minutes. Observe what collects on the magnet.
5. Repeat this same experiment with other brands of cereal. What do you observe? Compare the labels to see if the amount of iron differs.

Explanation: Total cereal does indeed contain 100% of the U.S. Recommended Daily Allowance (RDA) of iron. This iron can easily be removed from the cereal with any magnet. Since the iron is baked into the flakes, it is necessary to add water before the iron can be removed. This iron is actually added to the cereal in the form of very fine pure iron filings, which are readily attracted to a magnet.

The only problem with adding elemental iron is that the body cannot use it in this form. Before the body can use the iron, it must be oxidized to the Fe^{2+} form. This is done by the hydrochloric acid in the gastric juice of the stomach. However, most of the iron will be passed from the stomach before this can happen. So at best, your body is only using a small amount of the iron in the cereal.

Iron supplements usually contain iron in the Fe^{2+} form, also known as the ferrous form of iron. A common iron supplement is ferrous sulfate. This type of iron is not added to cereal, however, because it would drastically shorten the cereal's shelf life. Elemental iron never goes bad, but it may rust!

Electricity and Magnetism – Experiment # 9:
BURNING STEEL WOOL WITH ELECTRICITY

Objective: To discover the effect of friction on the movement of electrons.

Materials:
- 6-V lantern battery
- Two wires with alligator clips at each end
- Fine grade steel wool

Safety Precautions: Perform only under adult supervision. Wear safety goggles. Do not touch the steel wool during this experiment as it will be very hot. Do this experiment only on a fireproof surface. Have a fire extinguisher nearby.

Procedure:
1. Connect the wires to the battery and then to a small piece of the steel wool. Stretch out the steel wool so that it resembles a wire. Observe.
2. The battery will get very hot, so unhook the wires after a minute or so.

Explanation: The steel wool will become very hot and will actually begin to burn. This demonstrates that electricity can generate a tremendous amount of heat. Since the steel wool is a metal, it readily conducts electricity. Electricity is the flow of electrons. When the two wires and battery are connected to the steel wool, the circuit is completed. However, a tremendous amount of resistance is encountered as the electrons move through the very thin strands of metal that comprise the steel wool. A great deal of friction is produced as the electrons jostle against one another, generating a tremendous amount of heat. Eventually enough heat is generated to cause combustion of the steel wool. The steel wool easily combusts because it is very fine and has a large amount of surface area. Experiment with different grades of steel wool to see which combusts the easiest.

Electricity and Magnetism – Experiment # 10:
COPPER PLATING

Objective: To discover the chemical processes that occur in copper plating.

Materials:

- 6-V lantern battery
- 2 wires with alligator clips (available from Radio Shack)
- Strip of copper (or copper tubing)
- Iron nail (or other metal object)
- Copper(II) sulfate (available from hardware store as a root killer)
- Beaker or large glass jar

Safety Precautions: Perform only under adult supervision. Copper(II) sulfate is extremely toxic if ingested.

Procedure:
1. Place several teaspoons of copper(II) sulfate in the beaker. Fill nearly to the top with water and stir until dissolved.
2. Connect the copper strip to one wire and hook to the positive terminal (anode). Connect the iron nail to the other wire and connect to the negative terminal (cathode). Make sure the nail is shiny.
3. Place both the copper strip and the nail in the solution, and allow to run for about 30 minutes. Remove the nail and observe.

Explanation: A copper coating is formed on the nail, through a process known as electrolysis. This is a good example of an oxidation-reduction reaction. The Cu^{2+} ions in the solution are reduced to pure copper, which is plated onto the nail. The reduction reaction is as follows: $Cu^{2+}_{(aq)} + 2e^- \longrightarrow Cu_{(s)}$

The reason copper is used as the anode is because elemental copper will be oxidized into Cu^{2+} ions, thus replenishing the ions in the solution. This ensures that a steady supply of copper ions will be made available for plating. The oxidation reaction at the anode is as follows:

$$Cu_{(s)} \longrightarrow Cu^{2+}_{(aq)} + 2e^-$$

When removed from the solution, there should be a shiny coating of copper metal on the nail. A similar process is used commercially for copper-plating metals.

Electricity and Magnetism – Experiment # 11:
INDUCING POLARITY IN BUBBLES

Objective: To discover how a charged object can cause a neutral object to become temporarily charged.

Materials:
- Bubble solution
- Balloon

Safety Precautions: None

Procedure: Rub the balloon in your hair and bring it near some bubbles you have blown. Observe.

Explanation: The bubbles are neutral and the balloon is negatively charged due to rubbing on your hair. Yet the bubbles are still attracted to the balloon. Why is this, if only opposites attract? Why would a neutral object be attracted to a negatively charged object? In this case, the balloon actually causes the bubbles to be temporarily charged, which causes them to be attracted to the charged balloon. Because the balloon has an excess of electrons, these electrons repel the electrons on the surface of the bubble. Since the negative charges have been repelled, an abundance of positive charges now exist on the side of the bubble nearest the balloon. Since opposites attract, the bubbles are drawn to the balloon. The same thing happens when a charged balloon is stuck to the wall or the ceiling. The charged balloon actually causes the surface to be temporarily polar, resulting in the ensuing attraction.

Electricity and Magnetism – Experiment # 12:
MAKING AN ELECTRORHEOLOGICAL FLUID

Objective: To discover that viscosity can be affected by an electric field.

Materials:
- Cornstarch
- Vegetable oil
- Balloon
- Plastic cups

Safety Precautions: None

Procedure:
1. Add 50 mL of cornstarch to 100 mL of oil in a cup. Stir thoroughly.
2. Rub a balloon in your hair. Now slowly pour the oil-cornstarch mixture into another cup. As you are pouring, bring the charged balloon near the stream of fluid. Observe.

Explanation: The cornstarch forms a colloidal suspension in the oil. This is where the particles are not dissolved, but are simply dispersed. The mixture of cornstarch and water is an example of an electrorheological fluid, which is a fluid where the viscosity is affected by an electric field. In this particular mixture, the particles of cornstarch are temporarily polarized by the charged balloon. These polar particles then tend to line up with one another in a long chain in the presence of this electric field. This creates a chain of particles that are positive on one side and negative on the other. As a result, it becomes much more difficult for the particles to flow past one another. This alignment tends to restrict the flow of the oil, making it more viscous. The attraction to the charged balloon is so great that the flow will stop, and streams of the liquid will be deflected toward the balloon.

Electrorheological fluids are sometimes known as smart fluids, and have a wide range of applications. Since the viscosity of these fluids can be so quickly reversed, they have a wide range of applications, such as in shock absorbers, brakes, clutches, and hydraulic valves. A closely related group of liquids are termed magnetorheological fluids, where the viscosity is affected by a magnetic field.

Electricity and Magnetism – Experiment # 13:
GELATIN STALAGMITES

Objective: To discover the effects of a charged object on the particles of a neutral solid.

Materials:
- Unflavored gelatin
- Balloon

Safety Precautions: None

Procedure: 1. Pour a small pile of unflavored gelatin on the tabletop.
2. Rub a balloon in your hair and bring it near the gelatin. Observe.

Explanation: The particles of gelatin will arrange themselves in columns resembling stalagmites as the charged balloon is brought near. The gelatin particles are normally neutral, but become temporarily polar when brought near the balloon. The negatively charged balloon repels the negative charges and brings the positive charges closer to the surface of the gelatin particles. This polarity is transmitted to the neighboring particles, until you eventually have a long chain of molecules held together by the attraction of opposite charges.

The same process occurs in the electrorhelogical fluids examined in the last experiment. The cornstarch particles within the oil arrange themselves in chains as they are brought near to the charged balloon.

CHAPTER 13
LIGHT

Light is a type of electromagnetic radiation, which radiates outward in all directions from its source at the incredible speed of 186,000 miles per second (300,000,000 meters per second) in a vacuum. Other types of electromagnetic radiation are radio waves, microwaves, infrared, ultraviolet, X-rays, and gamma rays. Light travels in waves, as does all electromagnetic radiation. Light is the only part of the electromagnetic spectrum we can see.

The experiments in this chapter should help to shed some visible electromagnetic radiation on this illuminating topic . . .

Light – Experiment # 1:
INCANDESCENCE

Objective: To demonstrate why metals give off heat as they are heated.

Materials:

- Propane torch
- Metal tongs
- Coin (any type except post-1982 pennies, because they will melt)
- Cup of water

Safety Precautions: Do only under adult supervision. Exercise caution when using propane torch. Do not touch coins when hot. Wear safety goggles.

Procedure:

1. Heat coin over propane torch in a dark room until it is red hot.
2. Turn off torch. Observe the coin.
3. Place in a cup of water when finished.

Explanation: As metals are heated, they eventually become so hot they give off light. This is referred to as being "red hot." The coils on an electric stove are a good example of this. When metals become heated, some of the heat energy they have absorbed is released as visible light. Any object with a temperature above absolute zero (0 K) will emit electromagnetic radiation, which includes radio waves, microwaves, infrared, visible, ultraviolet, X-rays, and gamma rays. If a substance begins to emit visible light due to an increase in its temperature, then it is exhibiting incandescence. A typical light bulb gives off light when the tungsten filament becomes so hot that it glows. Any object above 500°C will emit visible light. At around 500°C, objects glow a dull red. At 1700°C, the temperature of a candle flame, a dim orange color will be observed. A light bulb filament is a bright  yellow-white, with a temperature of 2500°C. The sun's surface is at 5800°C, and is bright white. The hottest color is blue-white, which exists at temperatures above 6000°C, and is exhibited by some stars.

Light – Experiment # 2:
DO LIGHT BULBS REALLY BURN?

Objective: To discover what causes an incandescent light bulb to give off light.

Materials:

- Light bulb
- Propane torch
- Oven mitt
- Bucket of water
- Lamp

Safety Precautions: Perform only under adult supervision. Wear safety goggles. Use oven mitts to handle the hot bulb. Exercise caution with propane torch. Do not hold the bulb in the flame; instead pass it back and forth through the flame for no longer than 10 seconds. Make sure bulb is completely dry before inserting into lamp socket.

Procedure:
1. Wearing safety goggles and using oven mitts on your hands, pass the light bulb back and forth through the flame for no longer than 10 seconds. Do not hold it in the flame, and do not pass it through the flame for more than 10 seconds.
2. With your head turned away, quickly immerse the globe of the bulb in the bucket of water. The glass should break, but the filament should be intact. If the glass does not break, carefully reheat again and repeat this step.
3. Dry the bulb completely before placing into the lamp. Make sure the lamp is turned to the off position. Darken the room and turn on the lamp. Observe.

Explanation: A normal incandescent light bulb does not actually burn, but rather glows, through a process known as incandescence (see last experiment). As electricity passes through the filament, it becomes extremely hot, causing it to give off visible light. This is actually a very inefficient way to generate light because most of the energy used in an incandescent bulb is released as heat rather than light. Fluorescent bulbs are much cooler and more energy efficient.

To prevent the filament from burning, the inside of the light bulb is filled with a noble gas such as argon. Noble gases (the last column on the Periodic Table of the Elements) are very unreactive, and generally do not combine with other elements to form compounds. As a result of this atmosphere of argon, the filament cannot burn, since burning is combustion and requires combining with oxygen.   But when the glass of the bulb is removed, the tungsten filament reacts with oxygen in the air and burns in half as soon as the bulb is turned on. The white coating that coats the filament after combustion is tungsten oxide, a compound resulting from the reaction of tungsten with oxygen. The burning of the tungsten filament causes it to break in just a second or two.

This experiment helps explain why Thomas Edison had so much trouble making a workable light bulb filament. His first success came when he created a vacuum within a light bulb, which kept it from reacting with the air. However, an atmosphere of noble gas is far superior to that of a vacuum, since the argon exerts pressure on the filament, keeping it from sublimating as rapidly. A light bulb burns out when the tungsten filament eventually sublimates to the point that it wears so thin it breaks in half. Evidence of this can be seen in the dark spot on the inside of a used light bulb, which is caused by the deposition of the tungsten.

Halogen bulbs last much longer than ordinary light bulbs due to the presence of halogen gases such as bromine or iodine. As the filament sublimates, the tungsten atoms will collide with these halogen gases, which eventually deposit the tungsten back on the filament. As a result, the bulb can be manufactured to burn much brighter. Eventually the filament will break in half because the tungsten atoms are deposited back on the filament unevenly.

Light – Experiment # 3:
MICROWAVEABLE LIGHT BULB

Objective: To discover the effect of microwaves on a light bulb.

Materials:
- Light bulb
- Beakers or microwaveable glass cup
- Microwave oven

Safety Precautions: Perform this experiment only under adult supervision. Do not perform this experiment for longer than 15 seconds. Wear safety goggles.

Procedure:

1. Place a light bulb in a beaker filled halfway with water.
2. Place in the center of the microwave and turn on for no more than 15 seconds. Observe.

Explanation: The light bulb will light up when the microwave is turned on! This is possible because the tungsten filament within the light bulb is able to absorb the microwave radiation. As this filament absorbs energy, it becomes so hot that it glows. The filament within an incandescent light bulb does not actually burn, but rather glows as it becomes hot. The bulb is submerged in water so as to prevent microwaves from striking the metallic base of the bulb and reflecting off, causing damage to the microwave.

Light – Experiment # 4:

FUN WITH TONIC WATER

Objective: To observe the fluorescent nature of tonic water, and how to quench it.

Materials:
- Tonic water (must contain quinine)
- Clear plastic cup
- Black light
- Salt

Safety Precautions: Perform only under adult supervision. Do not stare at the black light, as ultraviolet light can be harmful to your eyes.

Procedure: 1. Completely darken the room and pour the tonic water into a cup under the black light.
2. Add salt to the tonic water, while it is still under the black light. Observe.

Explanation: The tonic water contains quinine, which is a highly fluorescent compound. Black lights give off ultraviolet light, which is invisible to the human eye. Quinine has the ability to absorb ultraviolet light from the black light and convert it to visible light. Substances that have this ability are termed fluorescent. The tonic water is especially beautiful under the black light while it is being poured. When salt is added to the tonic water, it quenches the fluorescence. The chloride ion of the salt reacts with the quinine molecule, producing a product that is no longer fluorescent.

Light – Experiment # 5:
DETECTING COUNTERFEIT MONEY

Objective: To develop a method for determining if U.S. currency is authentic or counterfeit.

Materials:
- Newer 5, 10, 20, 50, and 100 dollar bills
- Black light

Safety Precautions: Do only under adult supervision. Do not stare at the black light, as ultraviolet light can be harmful to the eyes.

Procedure: In a completely darkened room, place the various bills under the black light. Observe the color of the plastic strip within each bill.

Explanation: All new bills within the United States (except for the one dollar bill) have recently been redesigned. Each contains a thin, narrow plastic strip embedded within the bill itself, which is only visible if held up to the light. The strip within each type of bill will fluoresce a specific color if placed under an ultraviolet light. In the $5 bill, the strip will be blue. In the $10 bill, the strip will be orange. The $20 bill contains a yellow-green strip. In the $50 bill the strip will be yellow orange. The $100 bill contains a pink strip. These colors will vary somewhat under different wavelengths of ultraviolet light. It would be extremely difficult for a counterfeiter to place this strip within a counterfeit bill.

Light – Experiment # 6:
THE FLUORESCENT SCORPION

Objective: To observe the fluorescence of a scorpion under the black light.

Materials:
- Scorpion (Any species will suffice, but the Black Emperor Scorpion works very well. Scorpions are available from some pet stores.)
- Black light

Safety Precautions: Do only under adult supervision. Do not stare at the black light, as ultraviolet light can be harmful to the eyes. Do not handle the scorpion! Scorpion stings are extremely painful!

Procedure: In a completely darkened room, place the scorpion (while still in his container!) under the black light. Observe.

Explanation: Scorpions fluoresce a beautiful bright green color under the black light. This is due to fluorescent pigments in the scorpion's exoskeleton. This fluorescence is even visible in dead scorpions, though it is not quite as intense. The fluorescence of scorpions enables scientists to find scorpions rather easily in the dark with a black light. As a result, many new species of scorpions have been discovered since this characteristic became known.

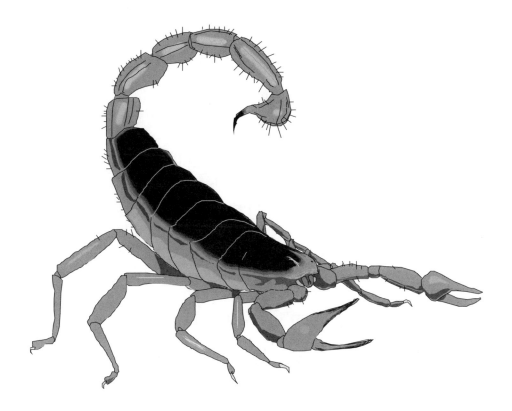

Light – Experiment # 7:
INSTANT RAINBOWS

Objective: To break white light into its constituent colors.

Materials:
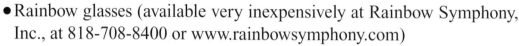
- Rainbow glasses (available very inexpensively at Rainbow Symphony, Inc., at 818-708-8400 or www.rainbowsymphony.com)
- Various sources of white light – fluorescent and incandescent bulbs, candles, etc.

Safety Precautions: None

Procedure: Put on the rainbow glasses and observe different sources of white light. Single point sources, such as a light bulb or candle, are particularly effective.

Explanation: The lenses of the Rainbow Glasses are composed of a special type of material that contains a diffraction grating. Diffraction refers to the bending of light. A diffraction grating has the ability to break white light into its component wavelengths. The diffraction grating is manufactured by scratching many narrow lines on a piece of glass with a diamond tip. The Rainbow Glasses actually contain replica gratings, which are made by pressing a thin sheet of plastic against the glass grating. When removed, an accurate imprint of the scratches from the glass is made on the plastic. The spaces between the lines form very narrow slits that allow light to pass through. As light passes through these slits, it is bent because it is slowed down. Each wavelength of light is bent at a different angle. As different wavelengths of light pass through the slits of the diffraction grating, they create what is known as an interference pattern, which produces the colors of the spectrum. The different colors of visible light are the result of different wavelengths.

A rainbow works according to a similar principle, with individual water droplets acting as tiny prisms. A prism works because different wavelengths of light travel at different speeds as they travel through the prism. As a result, each wavelength is bent at a different angle. This causes the individual colors to be visible. Violet light, with the shortest wavelength, is bent the most. Red light, with the longest wavelength, is bent the least. The breakdown of white light into its constituent colors is known as dispersion.

There are six colors that comprise visible light: red, orange, yellow, green, blue, and violet. These are easily remembered by the pneumonic ROY G BV. Some people have erroneously included a seventh color – indigo – in the spectrum. This seventh color was originally added by Isaac Newton, who first conceptualized the idea of the spectrum. He felt there should be seven colors to the spectrum due to the spiritual significance of the number seven.

Different types of light will produce different types of spectra. Fluorescent and incandescent light will appear different through the Rainbow Glasses. Neon light, which is primarily red, produces a very interesting spectrum. Sunlight will produce a different spectrum than artificial light. But do not look directly at the sun with your Rainbow Glasses!

Every element can be identified by its own characteristic spectrum if its electrons are excited and it gives off visible light. This is how scientists have determined the chemical composition of distant stars, including our own sun.

Light – Experiment # 8:
WHY ARE STORM CLOUDS BLACK?

Objective: To discover how light affects the darkness of clouds.

Materials:
- Two rectangular pieces of paraffin wax
- Aluminum foil
- Butter knife
- Candle or other flame source

Safety Precautions: Do only under adult supervision. Exercise caution when using flames.

Procedure: 1. Cut a piece of aluminum foil slightly smaller than the size of the wax.
2. Place the piece of foil on the surface of one of the wax pieces.
3. Place the other wax piece on top of the first, with the aluminum sandwiched between. The foil should not be visible.
4. Place the butter knife in the flame and then work it over the edges of the wax until the two pieces are securely melted together.
5. After it has cooled, hold it in front of you. The bottom will appear dark. Invert it. The bottom is still dark! This is even more noticeable if done outside or directly beneath a light source.

Explanation: This simple yet profound experiment demonstrates why storm clouds appear black. The aluminum foil reflects light, making the top seem much lighter than the bottom. This very clearly shows that dark is simply the absence of light. Clouds always appear white on top due to reflected sunlight. But if the clouds are too thick, then direct sunlight cannot penetrate them and they appear black underneath. If you could view very thick layers of storm clouds from the side, the top would be white and the bottom black.

Light – Experiment # 9:
ILLUMINATING LASER BEAMS

Objective: To demonstrate the Tyndall effect.

Materials:
- Laser pointer (available at Radio Shack for around $30.00)
- Chalk dust
- Aerosol can

Safety Precautions: Never look directly at a laser or point it at another person's eyes. Permanent eye damage may result.

Procedure:
1. Produce a cloud of chalk dust in the air, then quickly turn out the lights and shine a laser beam through the dust. What do you observe?
2. Repeat using the spray from an aerosol can or the fog produced in the shower.

Explanation: This experiment is best performed at night so that you can better view the laser beams. If dry ice is available, the fog produced when it is placed in water very effectively scatters the laser light. You may have seen movies where an aerosol spray or some type of dust is used to make a laser beam visible. The same effect occurs here. The laser beam is bouncing off each particle of dust or aerosol in the air, making the beam visible. You can also say that the laser beam is being scattered by the particles of liquid or solid in the air. This is known as the Tyndall effect, and can also be observed when a laser is projected through any colloid. The Tyndall effect also occurs if a flashlight or automobile headlight is projected through fog.

A colloid is a suspension of one type of particle in another. Fog, clouds, Jello, and milk are common examples of colloids. They generally have a cloudy appearance, as opposed to a solution, which is always completely transparent. Colloids tend to be cloudy because the particles are much larger than those in a solution. It is these relatively large particles that scatter light and make laser beams visible.

Light – Experiment # 10:
HOW FIBER OPTICS WORK

Objective: To demonstrate the principle by which fiber optics work.

Materials:
- Laser pointer
- 2-L bottle
- Nail

Safety Precautions: Never look directly at a laser or point it at another person's eyes. Permanent eye damage may result.

Procedure:
1. Fill a 2-L bottle with water. Poke a small hole with a nail on the side of the bottle near the bottom.
2. Turn off all the lights and hold the laser on the opposite side of the bottle from the hole. Shine it so the light passes directly through the water that is leaving the bottle. What do you observe?

Explanation: This experiment may require a little practice to get the best results. You may also want to adjust the size of the hole to get the best effect. You should be able to very clearly see the laser light contained within the stream of water. Incredibly, the laser light will follow the curved path of the water for quite some distance. If all of the laser light were entrapped within the stream of water, we would have total internal reflection. This occurs when all of the laser light is reflected internally within the stream of water, and none is lost to the outside.

This is the principle behind fiber optics, which are thin strands of glass fiber that transmit information by means of laser pulses. Fiber optics are replacing copper wires and cables as the preferred means of transmitting information. They are also used in decorative lamps, and by doctors to look into your stomach!

Light – Experiment # 11:
FUN WITH JELLO

Objective: To discover the effects of gelatin on a laser beam.

Materials:
- Laser pointer
- Different colors of gelatin, including red, blue, green, orange, purple, and yellow
- Food coloring

Safety Precautions: Never look directly at a laser or point it at another person's eyes. Permanent eye damage may result.

Procedure:
1. Add several drops of food coloring to a transparent container of water. Shine the laser through it. What do you observe?
2. Following package directions, prepare several colors of gelatin dessert (such as Jello).
3. Shine the laser through a transparent container of red gelatin. What do you observe?
4. Repeat with the other colors. What do you observe?

Explanation: Even though the laser passes through the solution of red food coloring, it is not visible within the solution itself. The particles of a true solution are much too small to scatter laser light. The particles of a colloid are much larger than those of a solution.

Gelatin is an example of a colloid, which is an evenly dispersed mixture that scatters light due to its large particle size. When a laser is shone through the red gelatin, the laser beam is clearly visible within the gelatin itself. The tiny particles of red gelatin reflect the red light of the laser, making it visible. It is for this reason the red gelatin transmits red light.

However, the laser is not visible in blue gelatin, nor does it pass through the container! This is because the blue pigment absorbs red light. Blue gelatin absorbs the other colors of light and reflects only blue light. Therefore, the red laser beam is not visible, since the red light is absorbed and is actually turned into heat.

Laser beams are very visible if shone through white fog, because white reflects all wavelengths of light. The only way our eyes can perceive a color is if that color is reflected. Certain pigments reflect certain wavelengths of light and absorb others. The wavelengths that are reflected are what our eyes perceive as color.

Lasers come in other colors besides red. What would happen if a blue laser was shone through blue gelatin? What if it was shone through red gelatin? Alternately light emitting diodes (LEDs) of different colors can be purchased very inexpensively from Radio

Shack. They can easily be hooked up to a battery. You can then clearly see, for example, what happens when a blue light is shone through blue gelatin. When using LEDs, make sure you match the voltage of the LED to the voltage of the battery you are using.

When you shine your red laser through the other colors of gelatin, what happens? Does the laser beam pass through? Is it absorbed? The results may surprise you. Read the ingredients on the packages to gain some insight.

150 More Captivating Chemistry Experiments Using Household Substances

Light – Experiment # 12:
MAKING A GLASS DISAPPEAR

Objective: To discover a way to make objects invisible.

Materials:
- Vegetable oil
- Small glass that fits inside of large glass

Safety Precautions: None

Procedure:
1. Fill the large glass about halfway with vegetable oil.
2. Place the small glass inside the large one.
3. Fill the rest of the way with vegetable oil. What happens to the small glass?

Explanation: When light passes through an object, it bends. This is known as refraction. The degree to which light bends as it passes through an object is known as the index of refraction. Every substance has its own index of refraction. The index of refraction, n, is calculated by the following formula:

n = speed of light in vacuum/speed of light in material

When light passes through water, for example, it is bent more than if it passes through air, so water has a greater index of refraction than air. Vegetable oil and glass have nearly the same index of refraction, so light is refracted at the same angle when it passes through both. Therefore, the small glass appears invisible in the large glass.

This experiment works best if the two glasses are made of the same type of glass. You may need to experiment with different types of glass to see which works the best. Pyrex beakers work very well. Baby oil will also work instead of vegetable oil.

A common magician's trick is to break a glass in pieces and place it in a glass of oil. He then pulls out the glass completely intact. The intact glass was of course already in the beaker ahead of time, but the audience could not see it because it has the same index of refraction as the oil.

CHAPTER 14
EDIBLE
CHEMISTRY

Everytime you cook a meal, you are performing a chemical reaction. Cooking is chemistry. The food you eat is made up solely of chemicals. Many of the tastes and textures of the foods we enjoy are due to the wonders of chemistry.

The following chapter contains experiments that you can eat. Have fun!

Edible Chemistry – Experiment # 1:
MAKING ORANGE SHERBET

Objective: To make sherbet by depressing the freezing point of ice.

Materials:

- Two cans orange soda
- One can sweetened condensed milk
- Quart freezer bag
- Gallon freezer bag
- Ice
- Rock salt
- Gloves
- Thermometer

Safety Precautions: None

Procedure:
1. Pour the two cans of soda and the can of condensed milk into the quart freezer bag. Seal the bag.
2. Fill the gallon bag halfway with ice and add a half-cup of rock salt.
3. Place the quart bag inside the freezer bag and seal.
4. Wearing gloves, knead the bag with your hands for about 20 minutes.
5. After about 20 minutes, remove the bag and enjoy delicious frozen sherbet.
6. Record the temperature of the melted ice-salt mixture in the gallon freezer bag.

Explanation: The sherbet made from this experiment is very good, and tastes somewhat like an orange creamsicle. The salt is added to melt the ice, and as it does, its temperature drops. Salt depresses the freezing point of ice. Since melting is an endothermic (heat absorbing) process, it draws energy from the surroundings, which in this case is the sherbet mixture. So much energy is drawn from the sherbet mixture that it freezes. The temperature of the mixture can get to about -15°C or even lower. That is why it is a good idea to wear gloves while performing this experiment.

  If salt was not added to the ice, the temperature would not go below 0°C. As a result, the sherbet mixture would never freeze. Anytime anything is dissolved in water, the temperature at which the water freezes drops. Since we are freezing water that contains a great deal of sugar, among other things, it must fall below 0°C before it can freeze. The carbon dioxide in the soda serves to give the sherbet an airy texture, since this gas will tend to escape as the mixture freezes.

Edible Chemistry – Experiment # 2:
HOMEMADE ROOT BEER

Objective: To make delicious, refreshing root beer using dry ice.

Materials:

- Dry Ice (Look in the Yellow Pages for a local dealer. Or contact a grocery store or ice cream parlor. They normally receive foods packed in dry ice on a regular basis, and will often give you dry ice free of charge.)
- Insulated gloves
- Sugar
- Root beer concentrate (available from the grocery store)
- Cup
- Plastic coffee stirrer
- Eyedropper

Safety Precautions: Use dry ice only with adult supervision. Never touch dry ice with your bare skin – it may cause frostbite! Use dry ice only outdoors or in a well-ventilated room to prevent buildup of carbon dioxide gas. Do not inhale vapors – inhalation of vapors may cause suffocation, since carbon dioxide displaces oxygen. Do not drink the root beer until all of the dry ice has sublimed.

Procedure:

1. In a plastic cup, place 17 drops of root beer concentrate and 21 grams of sugar (about 4 level teaspoonfuls) into a cup.
2. Add about 240 mL (8 oz.) of water to the cup and stir until most of the sugar and root beer concentrate has dissolved.
3. Now add a chunk of dry ice. Do not drink the root beer until the dry ice has completely sublimed. When it has, enjoy a cold refreshing glass of homemade root beer!

Explanation: The dry ice serves to carbonate the root beer by adding carbon dioxide. This makes the root beer slightly acidic. Dry ice is solid carbon dioxide, which does not melt. Instead it undergoes sublimation, which is the change from a solid to a gas. As the dry ice sublimes, CO_2 gas is released. A small portion of this gas will react with water to form carbonic acid (H_2CO_3). The equation is as follows:

$$CO_{2(g)} + H_2O_{(l)} \longrightarrow H_2CO_{3(aq)}$$

All of the CO_2 will not react with the water. Many CO_2 molecules will simply aggregate to form bubbles and provide the "fizz" that gives carbonated beverages their unique taste.

Edible Chemistry – Experiment # 3:
MAKE YOUR OWN PEANUT BRITTLE

Objective: To discover the chemical processes that occur in the making of peanut brittle.

Materials:

- Sugar (sucrose)
- Karo syrup (glucose solution)
- Butter
- Salt (sodium chloride)
- Peanuts
- Baking soda (sodium bicarbonate)
- Vanilla extract
- Stove or hotplate
- Pan or beaker
- Balance and measuring cups
- Aluminum foil
- Candy thermometer

Safety Precautions: Do only under adult supervision. Exercise caution with hot stove and with the boiling mixture. Use potholders to handle all glassware.

Procedure:
1. Add 75 g of sugar and 62 g of Karo syrup to a pan or beaker. Use 20 mL of water to rinse the remaining Karo syrup into the pan.
2. Heat slowly to boiling, stirring constantly.
3. Add 9.5 g of butter. Stir constantly and continue heating.
4. When the temperature reaches 138° C, add .3 g of salt and 55 g of peanuts.
5. Continue heating until the temperature reaches 154°C.
6. Remove from heat and add a dash of vanilla (about 1.5 mL) and 3.7g of baking soda. Stir vigorously.
7. Pour the mixture onto a buttered piece of aluminum foil. Spread thinly and evenly.
8. When cooled, you may enjoy homemade peanut brittle.

Explanation: Cooking is chemistry, plain and simple. Every time you cook, you are performing a chemistry experiment. Knowing the chemistry of cooking can make cooking much more enjoyable. The key step to making peanut brittle is the addition of the baking soda. At high temperatures, baking soda decomposes, giving off carbon dioxide gas. As this gas is released, it causes the mixture to rise noticeably. This gives the peanut brittle its airy texture. A similar process occurs in the baking of bread. The release of carbon dioxide gas by the decomposition of baking soda or the action of yeast causes bread to rise.

Edible Chemistry - Experiment # 4:
MAKE YOUR OWN FIZZY DRINK

Objective: To make your own carbonated drink.

Materials:

- Food grade citric acid (purchase from grocery or pharmacy)
- Baking soda
- Kool-Aid
- Aspartame (often marketed as NutraSweet) or sugar
- Transparent plastic cup
- Sensitive balance

Safety Precautions: Do only under adult supervision. Measure out amounts of above substances carefully. Too much of any of the above products can cause an upset stomach. Use sugar if allergic to aspartame.

Procedure:

1. Using a balance, measure out the following quantities: .45 g unsweetened Kool-Aid drink mix, .76 g citric acid, 1 g baking soda, and 3 grams aspartame sweetener (or two tablespoons sugar). Add to the cup.
2. Add about 8 ounces of water to the cup and stir until all powders have dissolved.
3. Enjoy your fizzy beverage!

Explanation: Fizzy drink tablets were very popular in the 1950's and 1960's, but were discontinued due to fears that the cyclamates used for artificial sweeteners were carcinogenic. A few years ago, they made a brief resurgence, using aspartame as the artificial sweetener. When a tablet is placed in water, carbon dioxide gas is released, producing a fizzy carbonated beverage. The fizziness is due to CO_2 gas that is produced by a chemical reaction between baking soda (sodium bicarbonate) and citric acid. The chemical reaction is as follows:

$$H_3C_6H_5O_{7(aq)} + 3NaHCO_{3(aq)} \longrightarrow Na_3C_6H_5O_{7(aq)} + 3H_2O_{(l)} + 3CO_{2(g)}$$

citric acid   sodium bicarbonate   sodium citrate

The fizzy drink you made utilizes the same chemical reaction to produce carbon dioxide gas. This same reaction is used for a number of other commercially available products, such as Alka-Seltzer antacid tablets, Efferdent denture cleaners, and Kool-Aid Slushies.

Notes: _____

_____

_____

_____

_____

_____

_____

_____

_____

_____

_____

_____

_____

_____

_____

_____

_____

_____

_____

_____

Notes: _____

_____

_____

_____

_____

_____

_____

_____

_____

_____

_____

_____

_____

_____

_____

_____

_____

_____

_____

_____

_____

Notes: _____

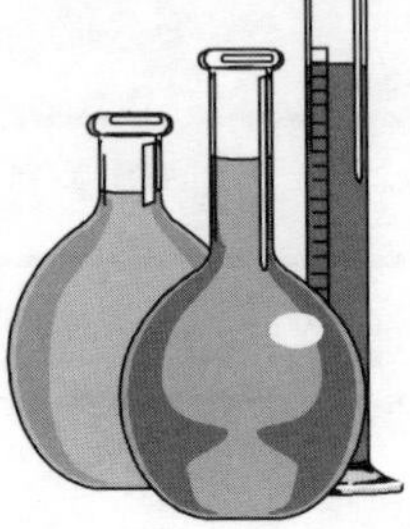

_____

_____

_____

_____

_____

_____

_____

_____

_____

_____

_____

_____

_____

_____

_____

_____

_____

_____

_____